C000215481

Non-verbal Reasoning

Assessment Papers

Up to Speed

10–11+ years

OXFORD
UNIVERSITY PRESS

Great Clarendon Street, Oxford, OX2 6DP, United Kingdom

Oxford University Press is a department of the University of Oxford.
It furthers the University's objective of excellence in research,
scholarship, and education by publishing worldwide. Oxford is
a registered trade mark of Oxford University Press in the UK and in
certain other countries

British Library Cataloguing in Publication Data
Data available

978-0-19-278511-4

10 9 8 7 6 5 4 3 2 1

Paper used in the production of this book is a natural, recyclable
product made from wood grown in sustainable forests.
The manufacturing process conforms to the environmental
regulations of the country of origin.

Printed in Great Britain by Ashford Colour Press Ltd.

Acknowledgements

The publishers would like to thank the following for permissions to
use copyright material:

Page make-up: eMC Design Ltd
Illustrations: OKS Prepress, India
Cover illustrations: Lo Cole

Although we have made every effort to trace and contact all
copyright holders before publication this has not been possible in all
cases. If notified, the publisher will rectify any errors or omissions at
the earliest opportunity.

Links to third party websites are provided by Oxford in good faith
and for information only. Oxford disclaims any responsibility for
the materials contained in any third party website referenced in
this work.

Introduction

What is Bond?

The Bond *Up to Speed* series is a new addition to the Bond range of assessment papers, the number one series for the 11+, selective exams and general practice. Bond *Up to Speed* is carefully designed to support children who need less challenging activities than those in the regular age-appropriate Bond papers, in order to build up and improve their techniques and confidence.

How does this book work?

The book contains two distinct sets of papers, along with full answers and a Progress Chart.

- Focus tests, accompanied by advice and directions, are focused on particular (and age-appropriate) non-verbal reasoning question types encountered in the 11+ and other exams. The questions are deliberately set at a less challenging level than the standard *Assessment Papers*. Each Focus test is designed to help a child 'catch' their level in a particular question type, and then gently raise it through the course of the test and the subsequent Mixed papers.

- Mixed papers are longer tests containing a full range of non-verbal reasoning question types. These are designed to provide rigorous practice with less challenging questions, perhaps against the clock, in order to help children acquire and develop the necessary skills and techniques for 11+ success.

Full answers are provided for both types of test in the middle of the book.

How much time should the tests take?

The tests are for practice and to reinforce learning, and you may wish to test exam techniques and working to a set time limit. Using the Mixed papers, we would recommend that your child spends 25 minutes answering the 48 questions in each paper.

You can reduce the suggested time by 5 minutes to practise working at speed.

Using the Progress Chart

The Progress Chart can be used to track Focus test and Mixed paper results over time to monitor how well your child is doing and identify any repeated problems in tackling the different question types.

Focus test 1   Similarities

Look carefully at the patterns given at the beginning of each line.
Notice the features that they all have in common. It is these
features that you need to find and match in the answer options.

Which one belongs to the group on the left? Circle the letter.

Example

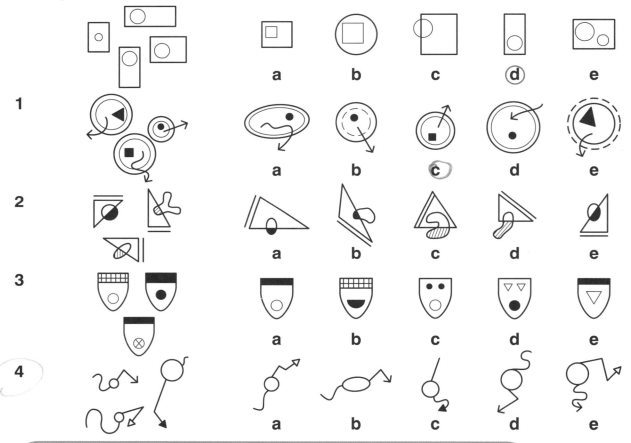

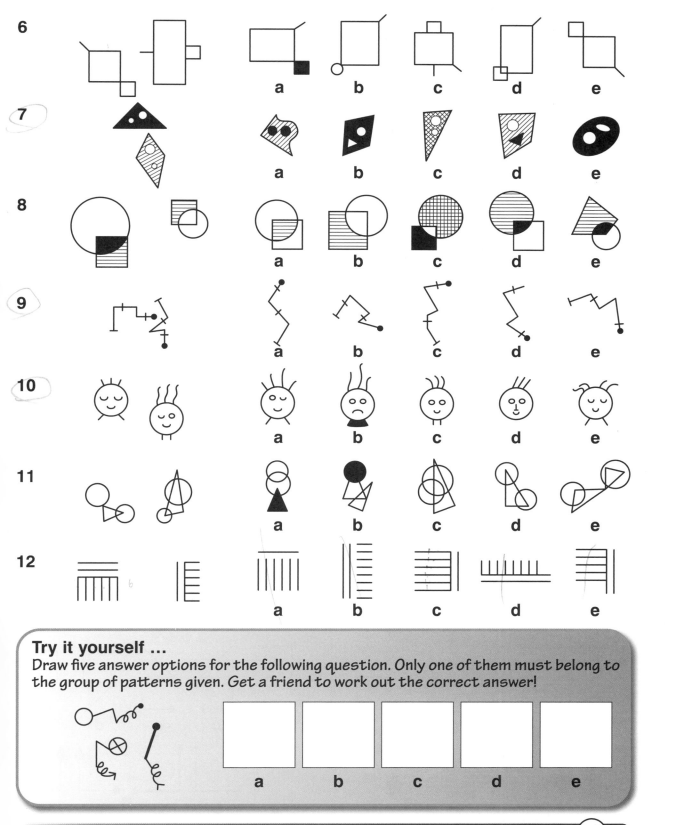

6

a b c d e

7

a b c d e

8

a b c d e

9

a b c d e

10

a b c d e

11

a b c d e

12

a b c d e

Try it yourself …
Draw five answer options for the following question. Only one of them must belong to the group of patterns given. Get a friend to work out the correct answer!

a b c d e

Now go to the Progress Chart … 5 *… to record your score!*   Total   12

Focus test 2 | Analogies

Look at the first pair of patterns – how does the first one relate to the second one? What are the similarities? What has changed? Now apply the same rule to find the pattern that will complete the second pair in the same way.

Which one completes the second pair in the same way as the first pair? Circle the letter.

Example

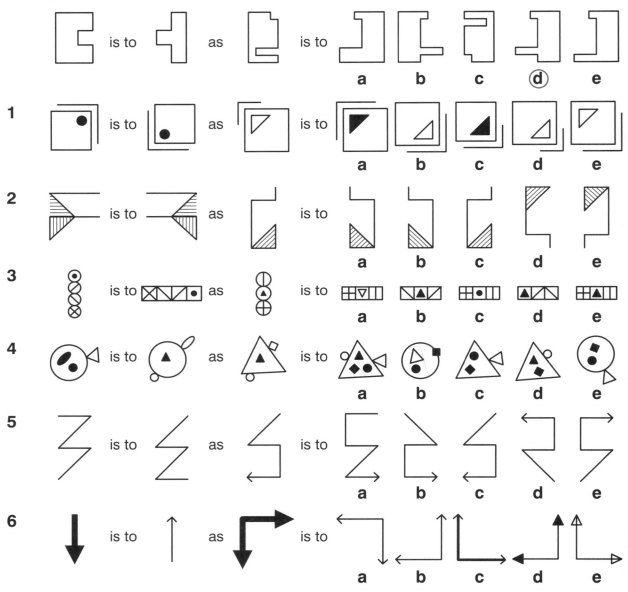

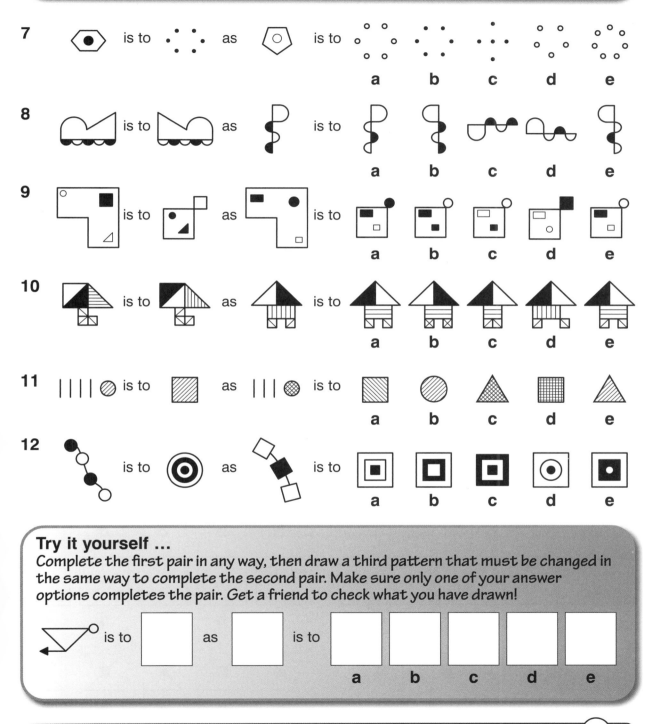

Focus test 3 Sequences

Look carefully at the given patterns to see what happens from one pattern to the next. If it is difficult to spot a clear link, look at alternate patterns as some questions are made up of two alternating sequences.

Which one comes next? Circle the letter.

Example

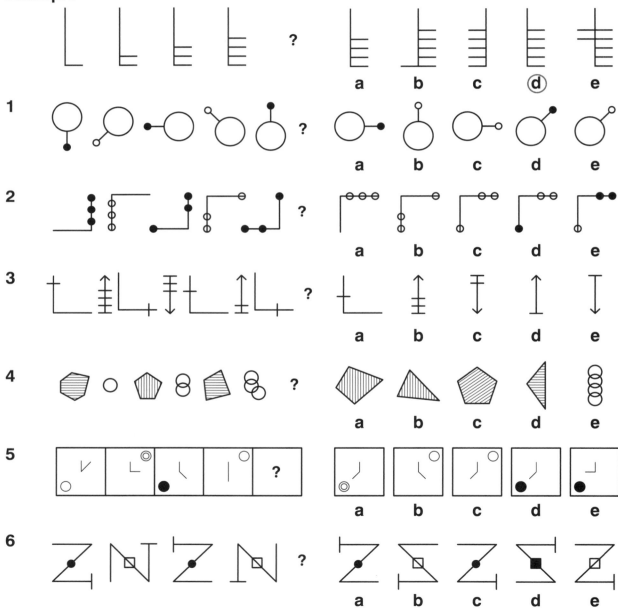

You may be asked to complete a sequence where you have to find a missing pattern. To solve these, you need to work back along the sequence as well as forward through the patterns given.

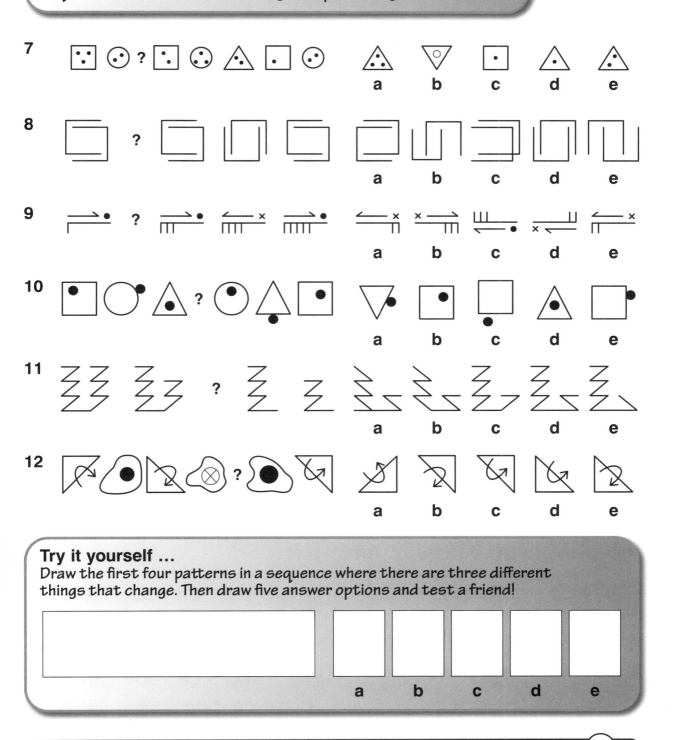

7

a   b   c   d   e

8

a   b   c   d   e

9

a   b   c   d   e

10

a   b   c   d   e

11

a   b   c   d   e

12

a   b   c   d   e

Try it yourself …
Draw the first four patterns in a sequence where there are three different things that change. Then draw five answer options and test a friend!

a   b   c   d   e

Focus test 4   Codes

Always start by looking at the patterns that share a code letter. See what they have in common, then check that particular feature does not appear in any of the other patterns. That letter position in the code will apply to the same characteristic in all of the patterns. You can then work out the missing code.

Which code matches the last pattern on the right? Circle the letter.

Example

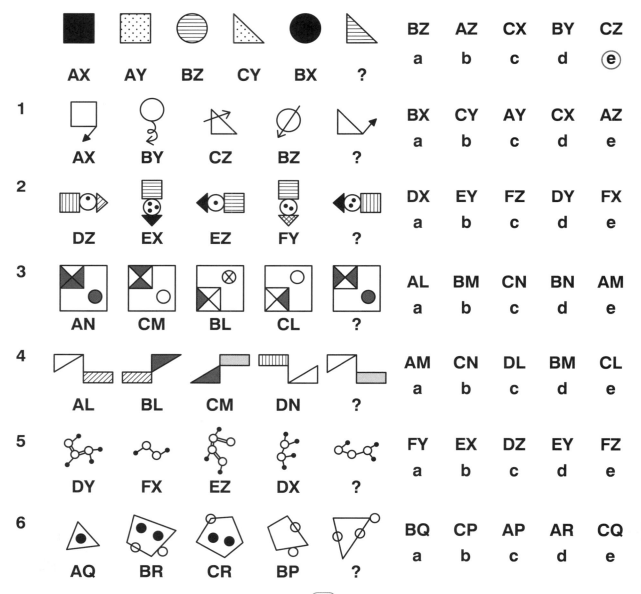

Some questions have three-part codes, with each part of the code linked to a different characteristic. To answer these, work through the same process, starting with a careful look at the patterns that share a code letter.

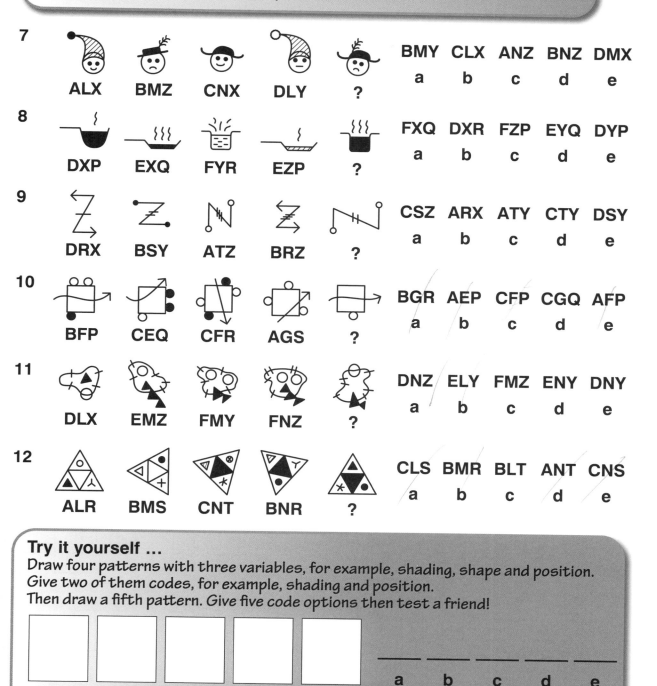

7

ALX   BMZ   CNX   DLY   ?

BMY   CLX   ANZ   BNZ   DMX
 a   b   c   d   e

8

DXP   EXQ   FYR   EZP   ?

FXQ   DXR   FZP   EYQ   DYP
 a   b   c   d   e

9

DRX   BSY   ATZ   BRZ   ?

CSZ   ARX   ATY   CTY   DSY
 a   b   c   d   e

10

BFP   CEQ   CFR   AGS   ?

BGR   AEP   CFP   CGQ   AFP
 a   b   c   d   e

11

DLX   EMZ   FMY   FNZ   ?

DNZ   ELY   FMZ   ENY   DNY
 a   b   c   d   e

12

ALR   BMS   CNT   BNR   ?

CLS   BMR   BLT   ANT   CNS
 a   b   c   d   e

Try it yourself ...
Draw four patterns with three variables, for example, shading, shape and position.
Give two of them codes, for example, shading and position.
Then draw a fifth pattern. Give five code options then test a friend!

___ ___ ___ ___ ___
 a   b   c   d   e

?

Focus test 5   Cubes

These questions test your ability to match a net to a cube or a cube to a net. Read the instructions carefully. You may need to identify the one that DOES match or the one that DOES NOT match.

Which net cannot be folded to give the cube on the left? Circle the letter.

Example

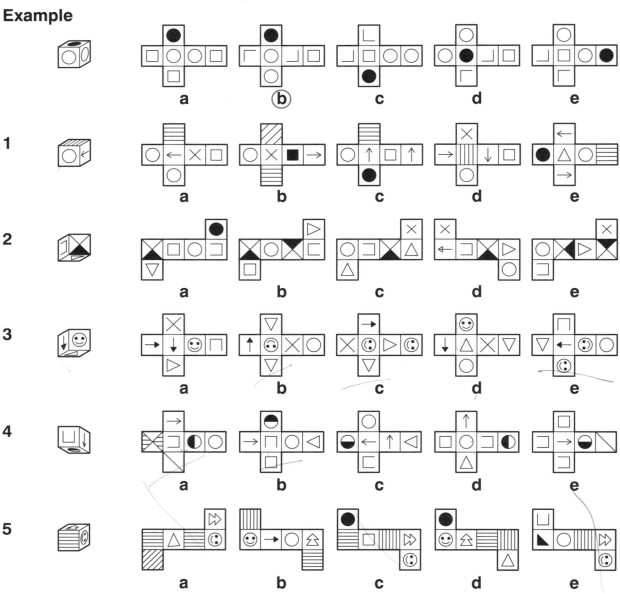

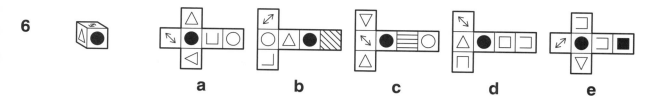

6

Which cube cannot be made from the net on the left? Circle the letter.

Example

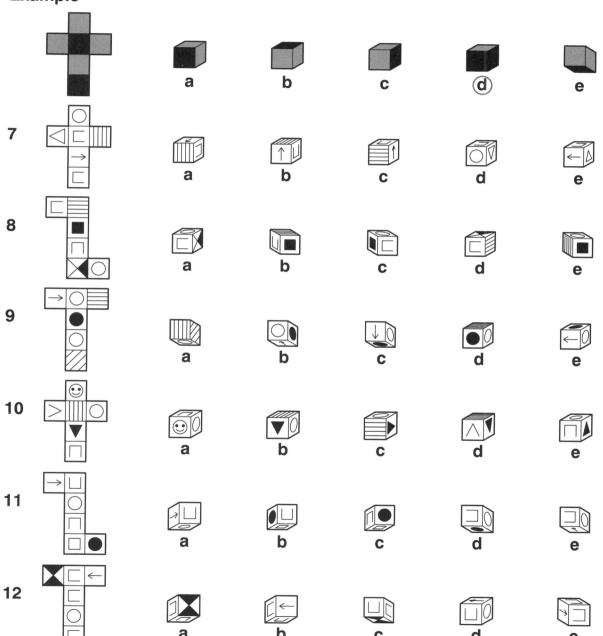

When completing a grid, you first have to find out how the grid 'works'. The whole grid may have a pattern, which can include line or rotational symmetry.

Which one completes the grid? Circle the letter.

Example

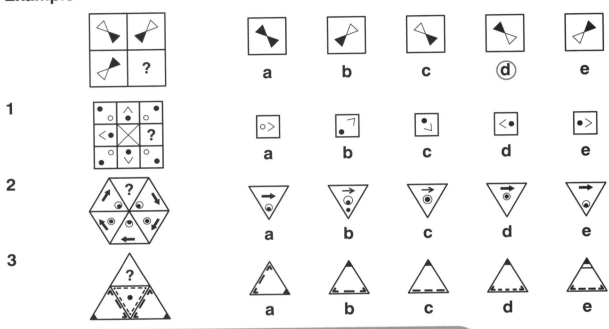

There may be different patterns along each row, with a link between the rows. You need to identify the link in order to find the pattern that will finish the incomplete row or section.

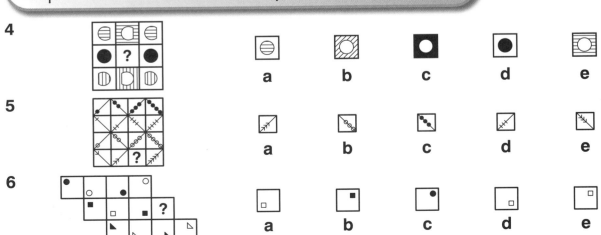

7

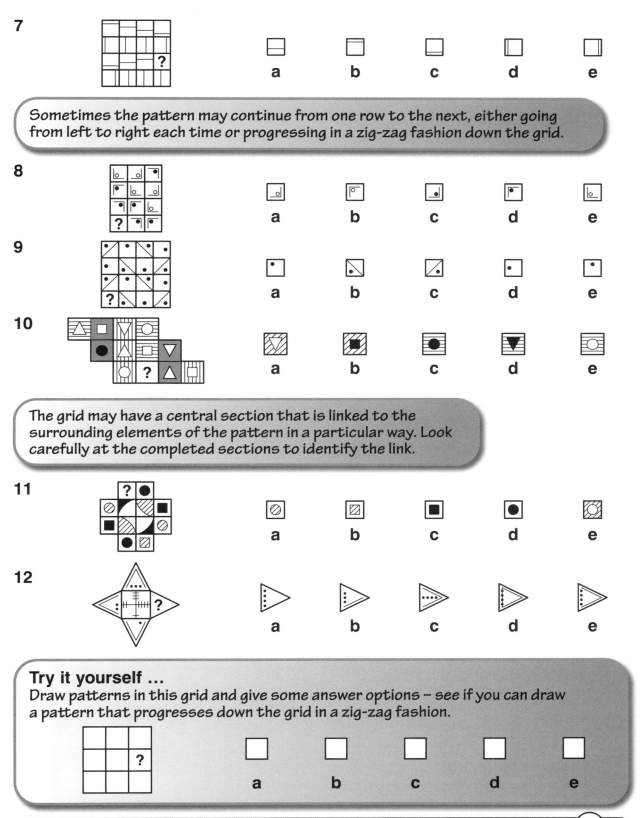

a   b   c   d   e

Sometimes the pattern may continue from one row to the next, either going from left to right each time or progressing in a zig-zag fashion down the grid.

8

a   b   c   d   e

9

a   b   c   d   e

10

a   b   c   d   e

The grid may have a central section that is linked to the surrounding elements of the pattern in a particular way. Look carefully at the completed sections to identify the link.

11

a   b   c   d   e

12

a   b   c   d   e

Try it yourself ...
Draw patterns in this grid and give some answer options – see if you can draw a pattern that progresses down the grid in a zig-zag fashion.

a   b   c   d   e

In these questions, the line of symmetry or reflection can be a horizontal line above or below the pattern, or a vertical line to the side. Reflection questions have a mirror line. When the mirror line is outside the pattern, the reflection is a symmetrical image. If questions ask for a symmetrical pattern, remember that could include rotational symmetry ⊕ → ⊕ as well as line symmetry ⊕ → ⊕.

Which one is a reflection of the pattern on the left? Circle the letter.

Example

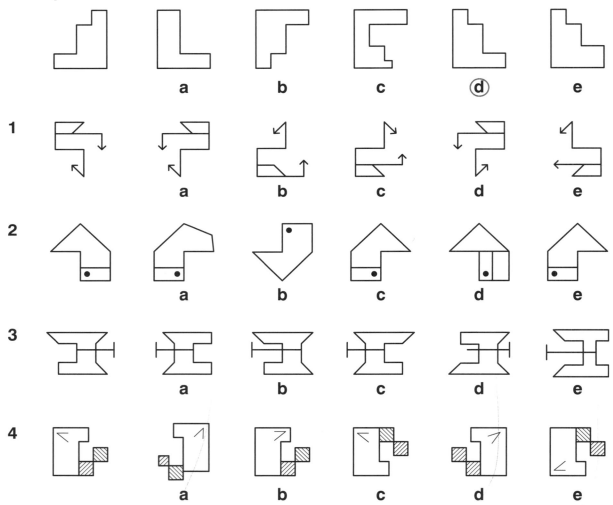

The mirror line can also go across the shape.

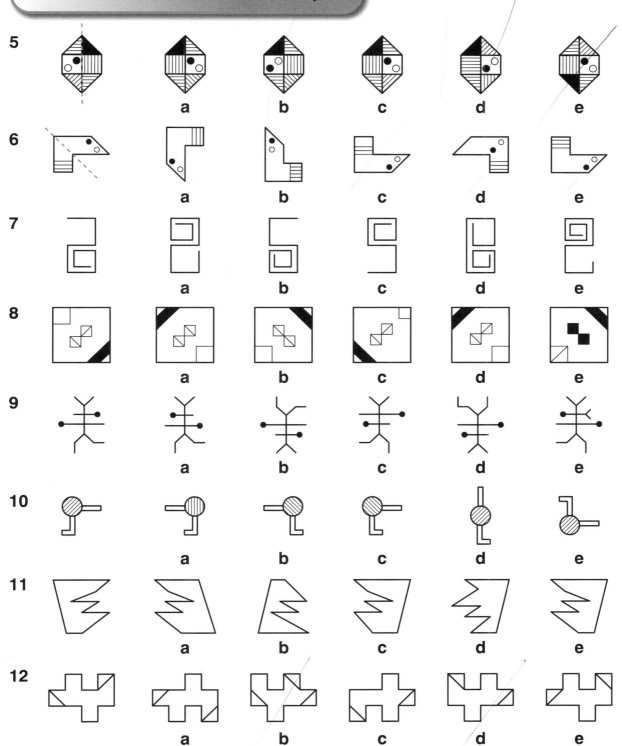

5   a   b   c   d   e

6   a   b   c   d   e

7   a   b   c   d   e

8   a   b   c   d   e

9   a   b   c   d   e

10   a   b   c   d   e

11   a   b   c   d   e

12   a   b   c   d   e

In these questions, you have to look very carefully at each of the two shapes in turn and then locate them in the answer options. They must match exactly, so you can reject any options that do not give an exact match.

Which pattern is made by combining the two shapes on the left?
Circle the letter.

Example

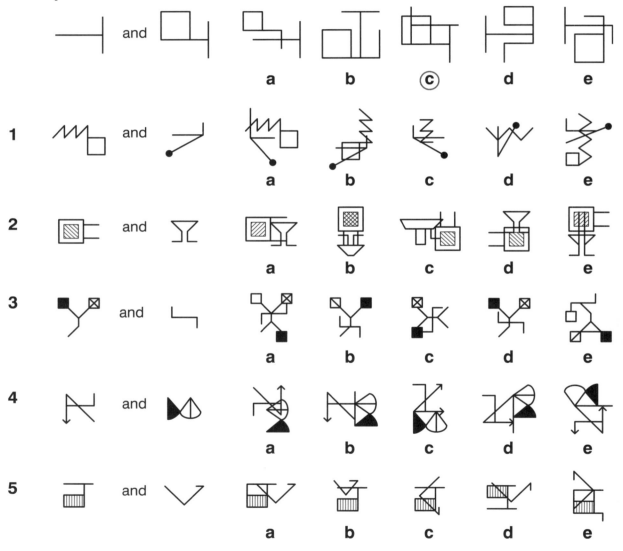

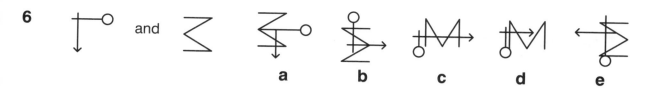

In these questions, remember that a shape may be rotated but not flipped over. Also remember that the two given shapes may share a line in a combined pattern but they will not share a 2D plain shape such as a square or circle.

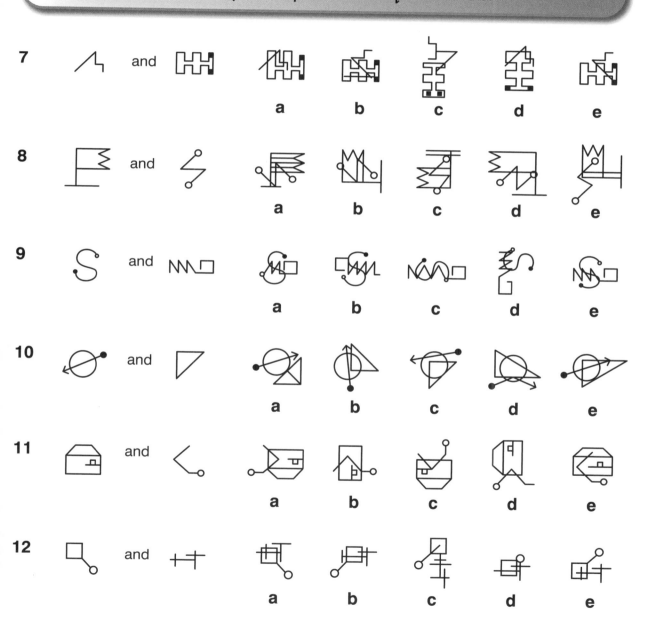

Variation in SHAPE is often a key feature of non-verbal reasoning questions, so always look carefully at any shapes used. In particular, notice the number of sides, angles and links between shapes. In this test, you need to identify the shape features that are used in order to answer the questions.

Which one belongs to the group on the left? Circle the letter.

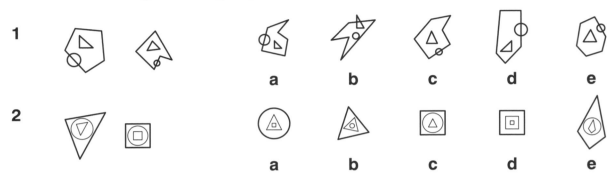

Which one completes the second pair in the same way as the first pair? Circle the letter.

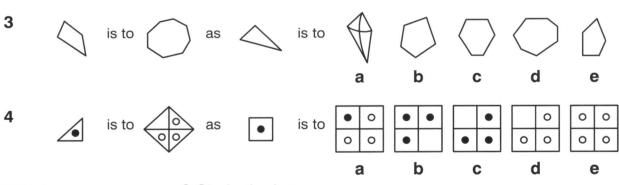

Which one comes next? Circle the letter.

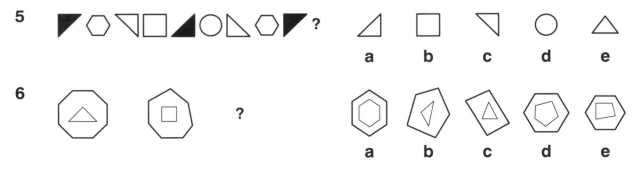

Which code matches the last pattern on the right? Circle the letter.

7

AX   BX   BY   CZ   ?

CY	BZ	CX	AZ	AY
a	b	c	d	e

8

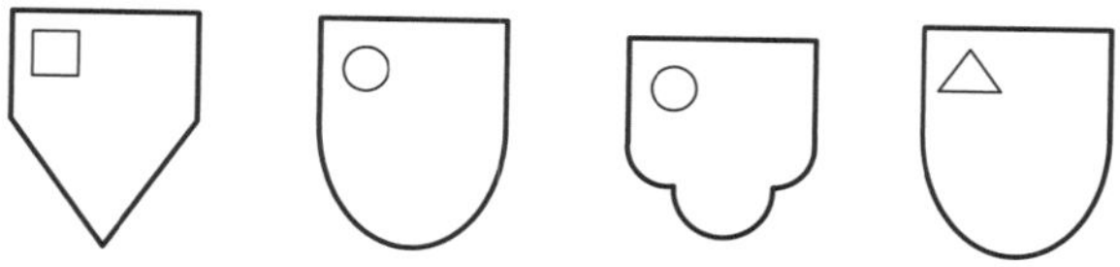

AL   BM   CM   ?

AN	BN	CL	CM	BL
a	b	c	d	e

Which net cannot be folded to give the cube on the left? Circle the letter.

9

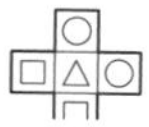

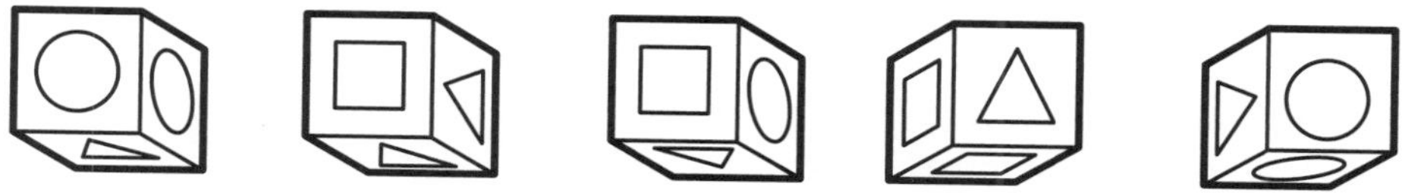

a   b   c   d   e

10

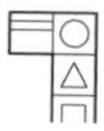

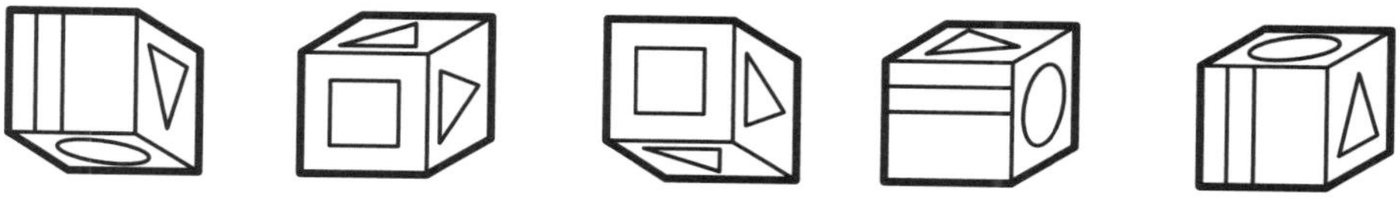

a   b   c   d   e

Which one completes the grid? Circle the letter.

11

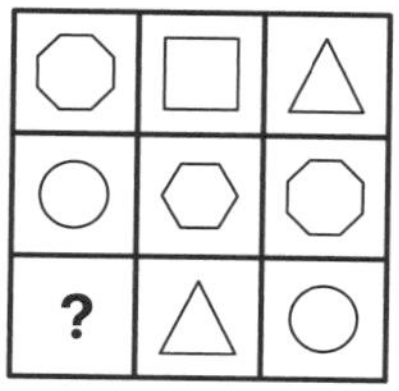

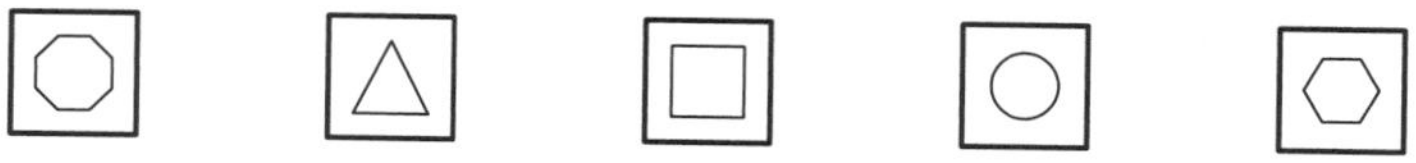

a   b   c   d   e

12

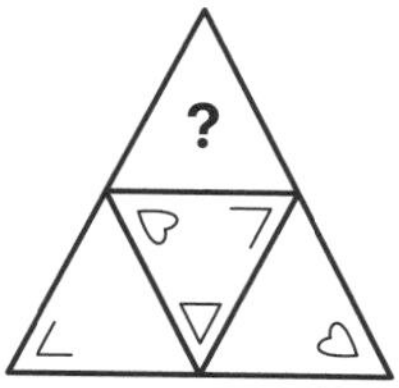

a   b   c   d   e

Often it is the POSITION of a shape or line within a pattern that is important. It might be the position of one part in relation to the whole, or it could be the position of one part in relation to another part. In these questions, look carefully at the position of each feature.

Which one belongs to the group on the left? Circle the letter.

1 

     a   **b**   **c**   **d**   **e**

There may be extra elements in the pattern that are not significant – identify them then ignore them!

2 

     a   **b**   **c**   **d**   **e**

Which one completes the second pair in the same way as the first pair? Circle the letter.

3    is to   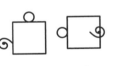

     a   **b**   **c**   **d**   **e**

4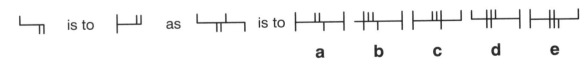

     a   **b**   **c**   **d**   **e**

Which one comes next? Circle the letter.

5 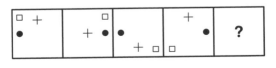

     a   **b**   **c**   **d**   **e**

6

         a   b   c   d   e

Which code matches the last pattern on the right? Circle the letter.

7

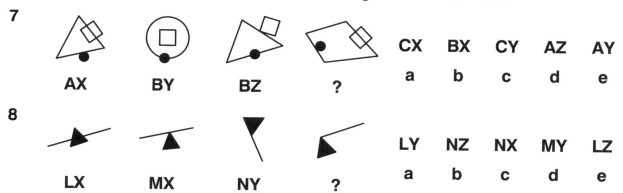

AX   BY   BZ   ?

CX	BX	CY	AZ	AY
a	b	c	d	e

8

LX   MX   NY   ?

LY	NZ	NX	MY	LZ
a	b	c	d	e

Which cube cannot be made from the net on the left? Circle the letter.

9

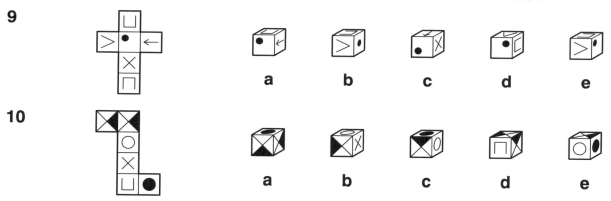

      a   b   c   d   e

10

      a   b   c   d   e

Which one completes the grid? Circle the letter.

11

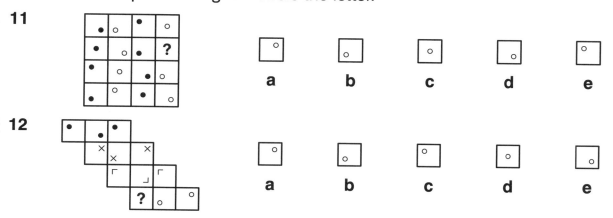

      a   b   c   d   e

12

      a   b   c   d   e

Always look carefully at the ANGLES in any shape, especially noting any right angles. It is also important to notice the angle or orientation of any line within a pattern. In the following questions it is the angles that will provide the information you need to identify the correct answer.

Which one belongs to the group on the left? Circle the letter.

1

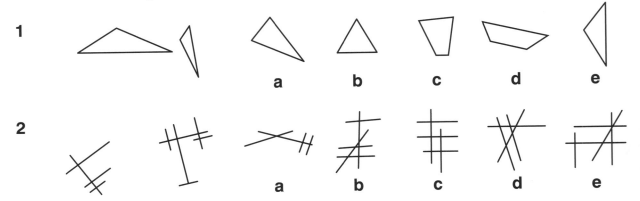

a   b   c   d   e

2

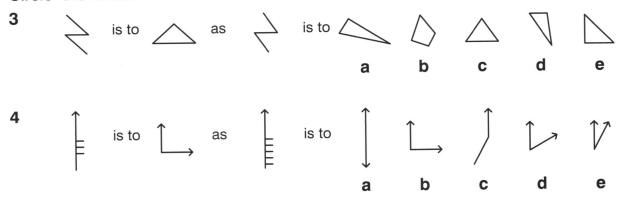

a   b   c   d   e

Which one completes the second pair in the same way as the first pair? Circle the letter.

3

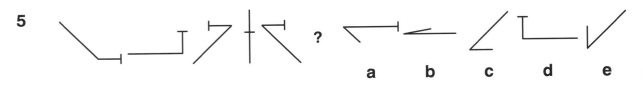

a   b   c   d   e

4

a   b   c   d   e

Which one comes next? Circle the letter.

5

a   b   c   d   e

6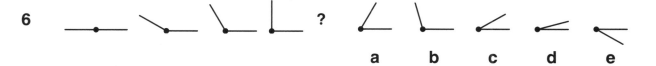

Which code matches the last pattern on the right? Circle the letter.

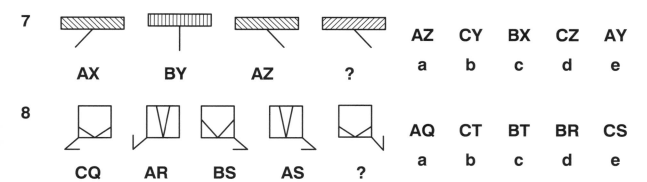

7

AX   BY   AZ   ?

AZ	CY	BX	CZ	AY
a	b	c	d	e

8

CQ   AR   BS   AS   ?

AQ	CT	BT	BR	CS
a	b	c	d	e

Which cube cannot be made from the net on the left? Circle the letter.

9

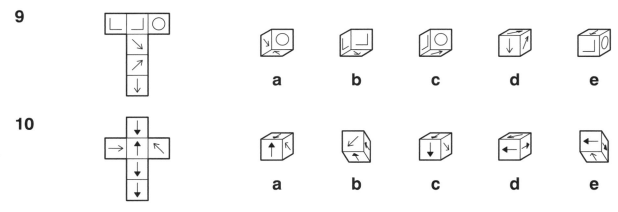

10

Which one completes the grid? Circle the letter.

11

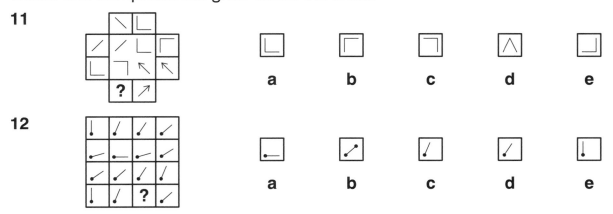

12

Count the NUMBER of lines, dots, crosses, intersections, and so on, very carefully in these questions as the number will give you the information that you need to spot a pattern and find the correct answer option.

Which one belongs to the group on the left? Circle the letter.

1

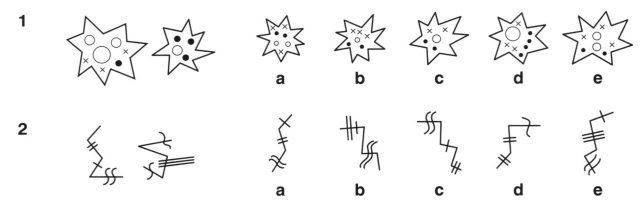

a   b   c   d   e

2

a   b   c   d   e

Which one completes the second pair in the same way as the first pair? Circle the letter.

3

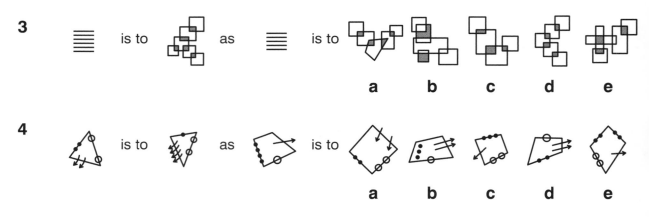

≡ is to ... as ≡ is to ...

a   b   c   d   e

4

is to ... as ... is to ...

a   b   c   d   e

Which one comes next? Circle the letter.

5

... ?

a   b   c   d   e

6

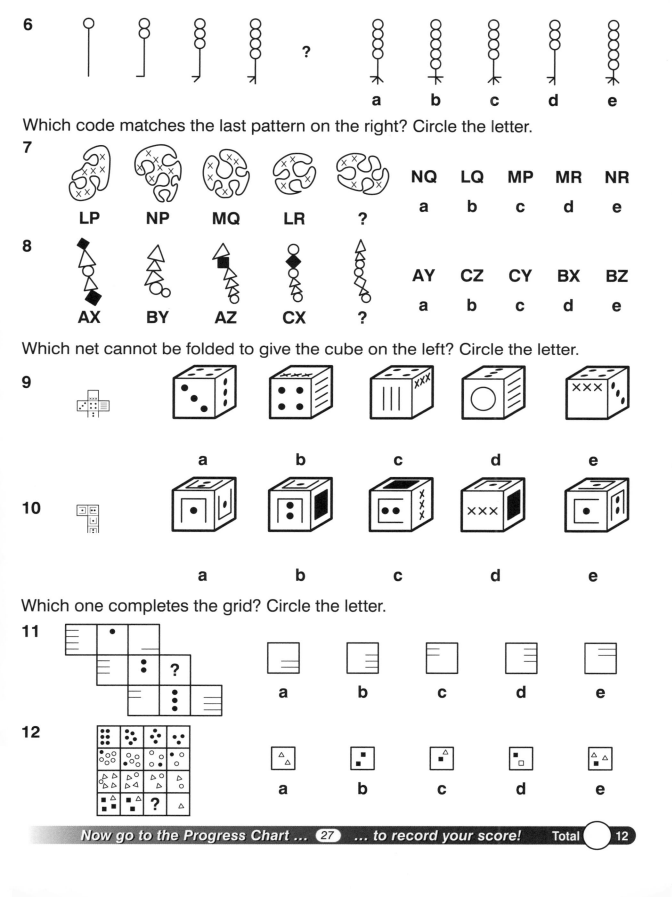

a   b   c   d   e

Which code matches the last pattern on the right? Circle the letter.

7

LP   NP   MQ   LR   ?

NQ	LQ	MP	MR	NR
a	b	c	d	e

8

AX   BY   AZ   CX   ?

AY	CZ	CY	BX	BZ
a	b	c	d	e

Which net cannot be folded to give the cube on the left? Circle the letter.

9

a   b   c   d   e

10

a   b   c   d   e

Which one completes the grid? Circle the letter.

11

a   b   c   d   e

12

a   b   c   d   e

Now go to the Progress Chart ... **27** *... to record your score!*   Total ◯ 12

Focus test 13 — Shading

Variations in SHADING are another key element in non-verbal reasoning patterns. Always look carefully at the style of any shading used, especially noticing the direction of any shading lines.

Which one belongs to the group on the left? Circle the letter.

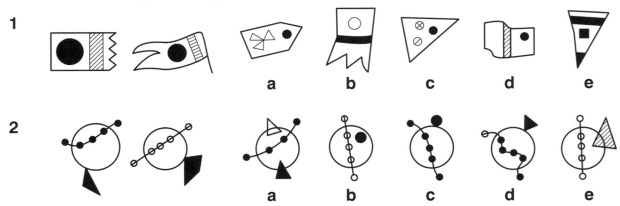

1

    a   b   c   d   e

2

    a   b   c   d   e

Which one completes the second pair in the same way as the first pair? Circle the letter.

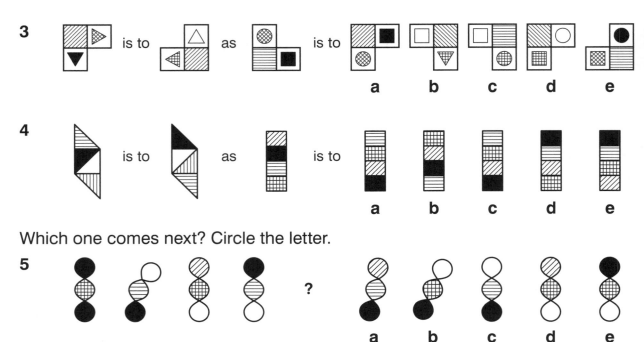

3
    a   b   c   d   e

4
    a   b   c   d   e

Which one comes next? Circle the letter.

5
    a   b   c   d   e

6

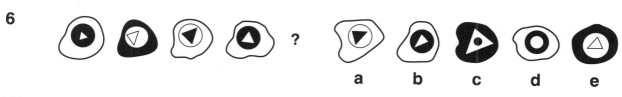

Which code matches the last pattern on the right? Circle the letter.

7

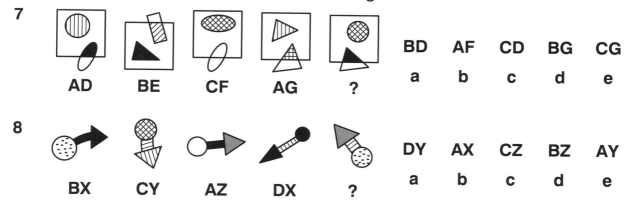

AD   BE   CF   AG   ?

BD	AF	CD	BG	CG
a	b	c	d	e

8

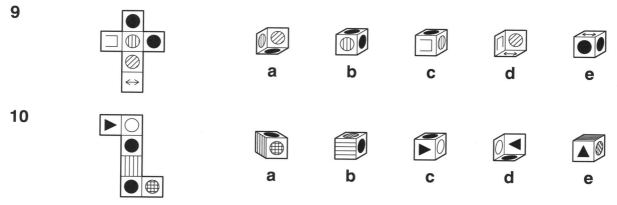

BX   CY   AZ   DX   ?

DY	AX	CZ	BZ	AY
a	b	c	d	e

Which cube cannot be made from the net on the left? Circle the letter.

9

10

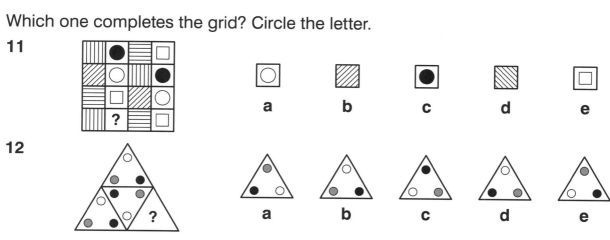

Which one completes the grid? Circle the letter.

11

12

Size

Within a question, the variation of the SIZE of different parts may be significant. This can be the absolute, actual size of a part, or it may be the size of one part in relation to another part of the pattern. Look carefully at the size of elements in the following questions.

Which one belongs to the group on the left? Circle the letter.

1

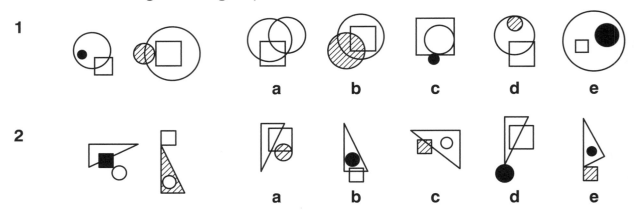

a   b   c   d   e

2

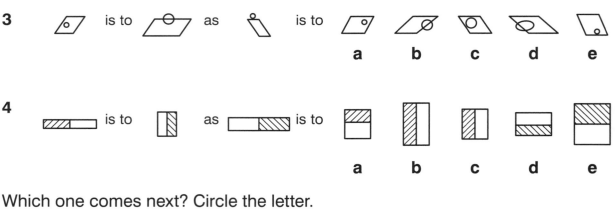

a   b   c   d   e

Which one completes the second pair in the same way as the first pair? Circle the letter.

3

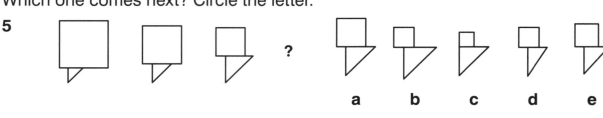

a   b   c   d   e

4

a   b   c   d   e

Which one comes next? Circle the letter.

5

a   b   c   d   e

Focus test 1: Similarities (pages 4–5)

1 **c** All of the shapes on the left have two solid-lined circles with an arrow from the centre to the outside of the shape.

2 **e** All of the shapes on the left are right-angled triangles with a shape across the hypotenuse (longest side) and a straight line parallel to the outside of one of the other sides.

3 **a** All of the shapes on the left have a band across the top of the 'shield' shape and one circle within them.

4 **d** All of the shapes on the left are circles with a curved line joined to the outer edge of the circle and a V-shaped arrow on the opposite side of the circle, pointing outwards from the circumference.

5 **d** Both of the shapes on the left have three linked shapes with one of the shapes shaded black and two white.

6 **e** Both of the shapes on the left are quadrilaterals with a small white square on the outside and with a short straight line projecting from the opposite side.

7 **c** Both of the shapes on the left are shaded and have two white circles within them. The two circles of differing size are what they have in common here.

8 **b** Both of the shapes on the left have a square overlapping with a circle with the non-overlapping part of the square shaded with horizontal line shading.

9 **e** Both of the shapes on the left have an irregular zig-zag of four straight lines, with a short line across one end and a black circle at the other. There are two short lines crossing the first and third sections of the zig-zag lines, starting at the end with the black circle.

10 **c** Both of the shapes on the left have three 'hairs', two 'eyes', a 'mouth' and two lines for a 'neck'.

11 **d** Both of the shapes on the left are made up of two circles which overlap or touch a single triangle but do not touch each other.

12 **c** Both of the shapes on the left have a set of six equal parallel lines joined along one side, with one or more additional lines parallel to that joining line, also equal in length.

Focus test 2: Analogies (pages 6–7)

1 **d** The second shape is the first shape rotated through 180°.

2 **b** The second shape is the first shape reflected in a vertical mirror line.

3 **e** The second shape has the circles changed to squares; the top one goes to the right and the bottom one is on the left of the new arrangement with the second and third squares in between. The patterns in each square retain their original orientation.

4 **c** The second shape has the small black shapes inside the larger shape converted to white shapes on the outside; the outer white shape becomes a black shape and moves inside the larger shape.

5 **e** The second shape is the first shape rotated through 180°.

6 **b** The second shape is the first shape rotated through 180°, with the bold lines changed to thin lines and the arrow head(s) changed to V-shaped.

7 **d** The second shape is made up of the small central circles arranged to give the outline of the first larger shape, with no change to their shading.

8 **e** The second shape is the first shape reflected in a vertical mirror line, but with the small black semi-circles changed to white, and white ones to black.

9 **c** The upside-down L-shape of the first pattern becomes a square; the shape in the top right corner moves to the outside of the top right corner, changing from black to white; the small shapes within the L-shape move into the square, with black ones becoming white and white ones becoming black.

10 **e** The second shape is the same as the first with white shading changed to black, black to white, lines and shading are rotated through 90° so vertical shading becomes horizontal and the diagonal lines in the small squares are now the opposite way.

11 **c** The second shape is a polygon with the number of sides equal to the number of lines in the first shape and with the shading style of the circle.

12 **b** The second shape is made by the shapes along the lines being superimposed on each other with the size changed so that each one forms a 'frame' around the preceding shape. The top shape is the central one in the new pattern.

Focus test 3: Sequences (pages 8–9)

1 **e** The line and small circle move 45° clockwise around the circle at each step and the circle alternates between black and white.

2 **c** The L-shapes with the black circles alternate with the L-shapes with the white circles; the circles moving progressively from the

vertical arm of the L to the horizontal arm. This sequence could also be viewed as pairs with the L rotated through 180° and the circle shading switched.

3 **e** The L-shapes alternate with vertical arrows and the arrows alternate between pointing up and pointing down. The number of lines across the arrow decreases by one each time.

4 **b** The polygons alternate with the circles; the number of sides on the polygons decreases by one each time and the line shading alternates between horizontal and vertical. The circle part of the sequence increases by one circle each time.

5 **a** The angle made between the two short, joined lines increases by 45° clockwise each time; the circle alternates from the bottom left corner of the square and the top right corner, and the circle style follows a repeating sequence of white–double outline–black.

6 **c** The Z- or N-shape rotates by 90° anticlockwise along the sequence with a black spot and small white square alternating in the middle of the Z-shape. The fifth shape in the sequence will be the same as the first here.

7 **d** The shapes follow a repeating pattern of square–circle–triangle, with the number of black dots within them following the repeating pattern of 3–2–1–2–3 along the sequence.

8 **d** The sequence is made up of two alternating patterns so the second will be the same as the fourth here.

9 **e** The top half-arrow of the shapes alternates between pointing right with a black spot and pointing left with a cross at the end; the lower half of the shape has an increasing number of short lines projecting down, increasing from the left end of the horizontal line.

10 **e** The shapes follow a repeating pattern of square–circle–triangle with the black circle alternating between the inside and the outside of the shapes and touching the edge.

11 **c** The number of 'zig-zags' in the shape decreases by one each time, beginning at the top of the right side of the shape.

12 **a** The right-angled triangle alternates with the irregular shape, and the triangle rotates 90° anticlockwise each time.

Focus test 4: Codes (pages 10–11)

1–6 Even though the following explanations give the letters in order, you may find it easier to identify features linking the second letter and then move on to the first letter.

1 **d** The first letter represents the shape (A is a square, B is a circle, C is a triangle); the second letter represents the arrow style (X is short with a solid arrow head and points out from a corner, Y is a curly arrow pointing out, Z is an arrow crossing the shape).

2 **b** The first letter represents the shading of the triangle (D has diagonal shading, E is black, F has cross-hatch shading); the second letter represents the number of spots in the circle (X is 3, Y is 2, Z is 1).

3 **e** The first letter represents the shading of the circle (A is grey, B has a cross, C is white); the second letter represents the proportion of black shading in the small square (L is one quarter, M is two quarters, N is three quarters).

4 **a** The first letter represents the location and direction of the rectangle (A is bottom right, B is bottom left, C is top right, D is top left); the second letter represents the shading of the rectangle (L is diagonal lines, M is grey, N is vertical lines).

5 **d** The first letter represents the number of small black dots (D is 4, E is 3, F is 2); the second letter represents the number of white circles (X is 2, Y is 3, Z is 4).

6 **c** The first letter represents the large shape (A is a triangle, B is a quadrilateral, C is a pentagon); the second letter represents the number of black circles (P is none, Q is 1, R is 2).

7–12 Sometimes, the code has three letters. Again, even though the explanations below give the letters in order, you may find it easier to identify features linking the second or third letter and then move back to the other letters.

7 **d** The first letter represents the decoration on the hat (A is a black spot, B is a 'feather', C is no trim, D is a black spot); the second letter represents the shape of the hat (L is pointy, M is flat topped, N is wide brimmed); the third letter represents the mouth on the face (X is a smile, Y is a straight line, Z is a downward curve).

8 **a** The first letter represents the style of the 'pan' shape (D is deep and rounded, E is flat, F is deep with two 'handles'); the second letter represents the shading of the 'pan' (X is black, Y is dashed, Z has diagonal lines); the third letter represents the lines above the 'pan' (P is 1 line, Q is 3, R is 4).

9 **d** The first letter represents the size and orientation of the Z- or N-shape (D is an elongated Z, B is a small Z, A is a small N and so, by deduction, C is an elongated N); the second letter represents the feature at the ends of the Z-shape (R is an arrowhead,

S a black dot, T a white dot); the third letter represents the number of short lines across the middle section of the larger shape (X is 1, Y is 2, Z is 3).

10 **b** The first letter represents the number of black circles (A is none, B is 1, C is 2); the second letter represents the number of white circles (E is 1, F is 2, G is 3); the third letter represents the position and type of arrow (P is a wavy arrow across the square, Q is a wavy line across a corner, R is a straight arrow across the square, S is a straight line across a corner).

11 **e** The first letter represents the number and position of the white circles (D is one circle across the line, E one circle inside, F two circles inside the shape); the second letter represents the number of short lines across the shape outline (L is 4, M is 5, N is 6); the third letter represents the number of black triangles (X is 1, Y is 2, Z is 3).

12 **c** The first letter represents the shading of the small circle (A is white, B is black, C has a cross); the second letter represents the shading of the smallest triangles (L is black, M is white, N has diagonal lines); the third letter represents the number of lines on the small 'star' pattern (R is 3, S is 4, T is 5).

Focus test 5: Cubes (pages 12–13)

1 **c** All of the nets except **c** have a face with an arrow that will point to a face with a white circle with the correct lines face above; in **c** both arrows point to a lined face.

2 **d** All of the nets except **d** will have the base of the black shaded quarter along the edge adjacent to the base of a white triangle; in **d** the black shaded quarter will be adjacent to a white circle.

3 **d** All of the nets except **d** have a face with an arrow pointing down beside the face with the smiley face and pointing to the side of the white isosceles triangle; in **d** the arrow points to a white circle.

4 **b** All of the nets except **b** have the face with the black semi-circle along the edge adjacent to the base of the U-shape; in **b** the base of the U-shape is adjacent to the white semi-circle.

5 **d** All of the nets except **d** have one of the lined faces with lines parallel and adjacent to the base of the 'tree' shape, in **d** the 'tree' face has the lined face to its side. Another way of looking at this one is all of the nets except **d** fold to give the smiley face to the right of the 'tree'; in **d** the 'tree' is to the right of the smiley face.

6 **e** All of the nets except **e** have the double ended arrow pointing into a corner that is shared by a face with a white triangle and a face with a black circle; in **e** the arrow will point to the corner shared with the black circle face and a face with a U-shape.

7 **c** Cube **c** cannot be made as its arrow face points to the side of the U-shape rather than being parallel to the sides of the U-shape.

8 **a** Cube **a** cannot be made as the open side of the U-shape is adjacent to the white quarter triangle opposite the black quarter triangle rather than adjacent to a white quarter triangle beside the black triangle.

9 **c** Cube **c** cannot be made as the arrow must point to a face with a white circle; in **c** the arrow points to the face with a black circle.

10 **e** Cube **e** cannot be made as the base of the U-shape must be adjacent to the top of the black triangle; in **e** it is adjacent to the white circle.

11 **b** Cube **b** cannot be made as the open side of the 'U's in both faces with U-shapes will be adjacent to the white square; in cube **b** the base of a U-shape is adjacent to the white square.

12 **c** Cube **c** cannot be made as all of the faces with U-shapes have the U-shape in the same orientation; in cube **c** one of the U-shapes is at right angles to another.

Focus test 6: Grids (pages 14–15)

1 **e** Directly and diagonally opposite squares around the outer part of the grid are a reflection of each other.

2 **d** The arrows at the outside of the hexagon are the same thickness, they are close to the outside edge and point in a clockwise direction around the hexagon and there is the same small circle pattern in alternate triangles.

3 **b** The outer three triangles have the same pattern within them rotated so that the dashed line is adjacent to the edge shared with the central triangle.

4 **c** The middle square in each row has the same shape as the squares either side of it with the shading of the background and the shape switched.

5 **e** The number of small lines or shapes in each square increases by one each time across a row and the diagonal lines zig-zag across the row.

6 **e** The small shape moves around the inner corners of the squares in an anticlockwise direction along each row, with alternate black and white shading.

7 **b** In the third row the horizontal lines move up the square progressively along the row.

8 **a** The L-shape moves around the corners of each square in an anti-clockwise direction, with the pattern continuing from one row to the next, from left to right; the circles are black when at the top of each square and white when at the bottom.

9 **d** Alternate squares along each row have a diagonal line, and the black spot moves around the squares, in a clockwise direction, from one corner to the middle of the edge to the next corner, etc. The pattern continues on the row below this time, moving in a zig-zag down the rows of the grid. Another way to look at this is down each column there is an alternate repeating pattern so the missing square will be the same as the second one in that column.

10 **c** The shapes follow the repeating sequence of white triangle pointing up–square–white triangle pointing down–white circle–black circle– continuing on the next row from left to right. The background shading is the same in each column within the grid.

11 **b** The outer pairs of squares round the grid have a square and a circle, with the squares alternately black or diagonal line shading, and circles also with the other shading, black or diagonal.

12 **e** The outer triangles have the same number of spots as there are short lines on the adjacent part of the central square and they all have an inner 'V' within the other sides of the triangle.

Focus test 7: Symmetry (pages 16–17)

1 **d**

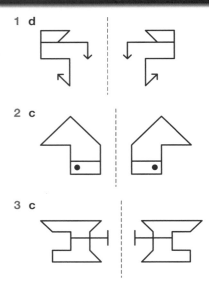

2 **c**

3 **c**

4 **e**

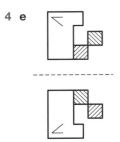

5 **a** The left side of the pattern is reflected onto the right side and the right side onto the left.

6 **a** The dotted line shows the line of reflection – use a mirror to see how each side of the shape will appear in the whole reflection.

7 **c**

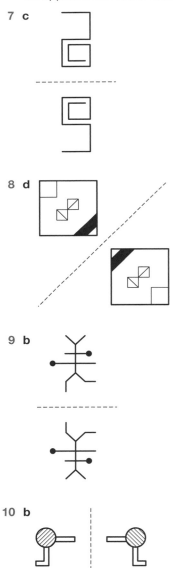

8 **d**

9 **b**

10 **b**

11 e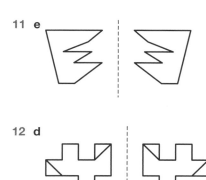

12 d

Focus test 8: Combining shapes
(pages 18–19)

1 b

2 d

3 d

4 a

5 c

6 b

7 e

8 b

9 e

10 b

11 c

12 e

Focus test 9: Shape (pages 20–21)

1 **d** All of the shapes on the left are pentagons with a triangle inside and a circle across one of the sides.

2 **e** All of the shapes on the left have a circle with a smaller shape inside and the same shape but larger around the circle.

3 **c** The second shape of the pair has twice as many sides as the first shape.

4 **d** The second shape has four of the outside shape joined together, with white circles in all but the top left shape.

5 **b** A repeating pattern of hexagon–square–circle alternates with right-angled triangles.

6 **d** The number of sides of the outer shape decreases by one each time and the number of sides of the inner shapes increases by one each time.

7–8 Even though the explanations below give the letters in order, you may find it easier to identify features linking the second letter and then move on to the first letter.

7 **c** The first letter represents the outer shape (A is a square, B is a circle, C is a triangle); the second letter represents the smaller inner shape (X is a circle, Y is a triangle, Z is a square).

8 **b** The first letter represents the large shape (A has a point at the bottom, B has a single curved line, C has a triple curved line); the second letter represents the inner shape (L is a square, M is a circle and so, by deduction, N is a triangle).

9 **b** All of the nets except **b** have the tip of a white triangle pointing to a face with a white circle, in net **b** it points to a face with a square.

10 **a** All of the nets except **a** have the open side of the U-shape adjacent to the white half of the face with two lines; in net **a** the open side of the U-shape is next to a face with a circle.

11 **c** There is a repeating pattern of five shapes octagon–square–triangle–circle–hexagon– along each row and continuing on rows down the grid, progressing from left to right.

12 **c** The shape in the outer corner of the outer triangles is the same as the shape in the opposite corner of the inner triangle.

Focus test 10: Position (pages 22–23)

1 **d** All of the shapes on the left have a heart shape within them and a circle across the outer line.

2 **e** All of the shapes on the left are made up of two crossing lines, one with a white circle at one end and the other with a black circle at one end.

3 **e** The second shape has the small circle moved to the top of the larger shape and the inside pattern now crosses the outline of the larger shape on its right hand side.

4 **c** The second shape has any short lines that point up in the first shape extended below as well as up, and the lines that point down in the first shape point up in the second shape.

5 **b** The small white square rotates round the inner corners of the square in a clockwise direction; the cross follows a repeated sequence of top–middle–bottom of the square; and the black spot alternates from the left to the right side of each square.

6 **c** The V-shapes alternate pointing up or down, the black spot moves down the side of the V-shape by half each time and the white circle moves progressively up the side of the inverted V halfway each time. The short line progresses steadily along the other arm of the V, whether it is pointing up or down.

7–8 Even though the explanations below give the letters in order, you may find it easier to identify features linking the second letter and then move on to the first letter.

7 **a** The first letter represents the position of the black spot (A is outside the shape, B is on the line and so, by deduction, C is inside the shape); the second letter represents the position of the square (X is across the line, Y is inside the shape, Z is outside the shape).

8 **d** The first letter represents where the line contacts the triangle (L means the line goes through the triangle, M means the line touches the tip of the triangle, N means the line runs along one edge of the triangle); the second letter represents which part of the line makes contact with the triangle (X is in the middle, Y is at one end).

9 **b** In all of the cubes except **b** the black spot is not in the centre of the face, in cube **b** it is in the centre of the side face.

10 **a** In all of the cubes except **a** the two quarter black triangles are in line, not touching and not perpendicular to each other, except in cube **a** where they are perpendicular to each other.

11 **e** In each diagonal row across the grid from top left to bottom right, the circles are in the same position within those squares, with the circle colour the same down each column of the grid.

12 **a** Along each row within the grid the inner small shape alternates between diagonally opposite positions with the squares.

Focus test 11: Angle (pages 8–9)

1 **e** All of the shapes on the left are triangles with two acute angles and one obtuse angle.

2 **c** All of the shapes on the left are made up of lines which only cross each other at right angles.

3 **c** The second triangle has the same base angles as the angles in the zig-zag pattern of the first shape.

4 **e** The number of short lines on the first shape gives the number of 30° sectors the bottom half of the line will rotate through, anticlockwise, to give the second shape, adding an arrow head at the end of the rotated line.

5 **d** The short line with the T-end rotates through 90° each time and the longer line rotates through 45° each time, both rotating in an anti-clockwise direction.

6 **a** The section of the first shape which begins on the left rotates clockwise by 30° each time.

7–8 Even though the explanations below give the letters in order, you may find it easier to identify features linking the second letter and then move on to the first letter.

7 **d** The first letter represents the shading of the rectangle (A is 'downhill' diagonal lines, B is vertical lines so, by deduction, C has 'uphill' diagonal lines); the second letter represents the angle of the short line below the rectangle (X is 45° to the left, Y is perpendicular to the rectangle, Z is 45° to the right).

8 **b** The first letter represents the angle made by the V-lines inside the square (A is an acute angle, B is a right angle, C is an obtuse angle); the second letter represents the position and orientation of the short V-shape outside the square (Q is at the bottom left corner pointing horizontally, R is at the bottom left corner pointing vertically, S is at the bottom right corner pointing horizontally so, by deduction, T is at the bottom right corner pointing vertically).

9 **d** The three faces with arrows are all in a line in the net so those three faces cannot be adjacent to each other in the cube.

10 **b** The faces with the bold arrows always point directly towards or away from each other and in cube **b** the two side faces have the arrows parallel to each other.

11 **c** Looking clockwise round the grid, the second of each outer pair of squares has the same pattern as that in the adjacent corner of the larger inner square.

12 **d** The angle formed by the 'pin' shape as it moves clockwise from a vertical position to a horizontal position and back again, increases progressively along each line of the grid, moving from one row to the next left to right then right to left down the grid.

1 **e** All of the shapes on the left have four circles within a 14-sided irregular polygon.

2 **b** All of the shapes on the left are made up of four straight lines forming an irregular zig-zag, crossed by two wavy lines and three straight lines.

3 **d** The second shape has the same number of squares as there are lines in the first shape. Only the areas where the squares overlap are shaded grey.

4 **d** The second shape has the same number of white circles across its outer line, with half the number of small black spots and twice the number of arrows (pointing outwards) as the first shape.

5 **b** The number of lines forming the zig-zag pattern decreases by one each time.

6 **e** The number of circles increases by one each time and the number of short lines also increases by one, at 45° to the previous lines and added in an anticlockwise direction.

7–8 Even though the explanations below give the letters in order, you may find it easier to identify features linking the second letter and then move on to the first letter.

7 **d** The first letter represents the number of loops or 'inlets' into the larger shape (L is 3, M is 4, N is 5); the second letter represents the number of crosses (P is 6, Q is 5, R is 4).

8 **c** The first letter represents the number of circles in each shape (A is 1, B is 2, C is 3) and the second letter represents the number of triangles in each shape (X is 2, Y is 3, Z is 4).

9 **c** The three faces showing on the cube cannot all be in a line in the net.

10 **d** When a face with the base of U-shape and one spot is adjacent to one with the base of a U-shape and two spots, if the third adjacent face has a U-shape with one spot, that U-shape will be perpendicular to the other face with a U-shape and one spot, not aligned with it.

11 **a** Moving down and right along the diagonal lines of the grid, the line pattern in each square in the final column increases by one each time.

12 **c** The number of shapes in each square decreases by one each time along each row; the shading pattern along alternate rows is similar, with white and black shading patterns swapped.

1 **d** Both of the shapes on the left have a bar with diagonal shading and a black circle within them.

2 **c** Both of the shapes on the left have a connected line of five circles crossing a larger circle, with three of the smaller circles within the larger one, and a black shape touching the outside of the large circle.

3 **c** The L-shape of three squares in the first shape is rotated through 180°, and in the smaller shapes the diagonal cross-hatch shading becomes straight grid shading and the black shape becomes white.

4 **e** The outer shape remains the same in the second shape, with the shading style of the four inner parts all moving up one place and the shading from the top small section filling the section at the bottom.

5 **b** The shading of the top circle follows the repeating pattern of black–white–diagonal lines; the middle circle alternates between cross-grid shading and horizontal line shading; and the bottom circle has two black, then two white along the sequence. The angle is not part of the sequence.

6 **e** The black shading moves out from one section to the next one along the sequence, then returning to the central section once at the outermost section of the shape. The missing shape will be similar to the second one here.

7–8 Even though the explanations below give the letters in order, you may find it easier to identify features linking the second letter and then move on to the first letter.

7 **c** The first letter represents the shading style of the shape inside the square (A is vertical lines, B is black, C is diagonal cross-hatch); the second letter represents the shading within the square of the overlapped section of the second shape (D is black, E is diagonal lines, F is white, G is straight grid lines).

8 **d** The first letter represents the shading of the circle (A is white, B is dashes, C is diagonal cross-hatch, D is black); the second letter represents the shading of the arrowhead (X is black, Y is lines, Z is grey).

9 **a** The net shows that, if the face with the 'straight-line' shaded circle has those lines vertical then the 'diagonal-line' circle face must be above or below it, not alongside it.

10 **e** The tip of the black triangle points towards the face with the white circle, not the lined face as in cube **e**.

11 **c** There is a repeating pattern of six styles: vertical lines–black circle–horizontal lines–white square–diagonal lines–white circle–moving along the rows from left to right and progressing down the grid.

12 **b** The outer triangles of the grid are all the same. Also, at the line where the outer and inner triangles meet, the colours of the two dots are swapped.

Focus test 14: Size (pages 30–31)

1 **d** Both of the shapes on the left have a white circle that is larger than the square which is larger than the shaded circle with only one overlap.

2 **b** Both of the shapes on the left are made up of the same sized right-angled triangle, the same sized square and the same sized circle.

3 **c** The second shape has all the same parts as the first shape with the circle at twice the size and the parallelogram double the width.

4 **c** The second shape has the first two rectangles which are end to end placed next to each other and rotated though 90° anticlockwise with the shading on the left side in the first shape moving to the right half of the second shape.

5 **b** The square gets progressively smaller and the triangle at its base gets progressively larger.

6 **a** The triangles are alternately pointing up or down and increasing in height along the sequence; the squares alternate between black and white.

7–8 Even though the explanations below give the letters in order, you may find it easier to identify features linking the second letter and then move on to the first letter.

7 **e** The first letter represents the line pattern at the bottom of the shape (A is an L-shape, B is an inverted T-shape so, by deduction, C is a reverse L-shape); the second letter represents the size of the Z-shape (X is large, Y is medium, Z is small).

8 **b** The first letter represents the size and type of arrow (D is large head with double line, E is small head with double line, F has a single line); the second letter represents the size of the circle (M is small, L is medium, N is large).

9 **a** When a face with a white square is next to the face with the small black square it must have the face with the small white circle on the top.

10 **e** The face with the U-shape will be opposite the face with the large white circle and cannot be adjacent to it. If the U-shape face is on the front

with the small white square underneath, the right hand face must be the small white circle.

11 **c** The repeating sequence of shapes along the rows of the grid is big circle–little circle–big square–big square–little square, with the colour sequence black–white–white–.

12 **e** The same shape is repeated down each column, alternating between small and large.

Focus test 15 (pages 32–33)

1 **e** Both of the shapes on the left have a quadrilateral with a V-shape crossing them, with the same pattern at both ends of the V-shape.

2 **d** Both of the shapes on the left are triangles crossed by a curved line which has: two small crosses on it inside the triangle; one cross outside the triangle and a different pattern at the other end. There is also a small shape overlapping one side of the triangle with the outer part shaded.

3 **d** Both of the shapes on the left have two parallel lines, one solid and one dashed, which come from the corner of a square; there is a perpendicular line at the other end which may or may not have other features.

4 **a** The two short lines projecting from one corner of the square rotate clockwise round the square at each step; the circles are alternately in the centre of the square or rotating around the edges of the square in a clockwise direction.

5 **d** The number of 'pins' crossing the line decreases along the sequence, with the pins alternately black headed projecting up over the line and white headed projecting down over the line. The row of pins commences with a short one closest to the white circle at the end of the long line.

6 **c** Large white squares alternate with small, shaded squares; the black spot inside the white square alternates between the top left and bottom right corners. The number of black spots along the outer edge alternates between being below and above the square and increases by one each time along the sequence.

7 **e** The face with the cross cannot be adjacent to the face with the U-shape. Also, if the net was folded with the cross on the front and the circle on the right then the top face must be a V-shape.

8 **d** The face with the black crescent cannot have the curve of the crescent along the edge of a face with a downward pointing arrow.

9 **b** The face with the white circle cannot be

adjacent to the black triangle of a half shaded face and the top of the face with a V-shape.

10 c

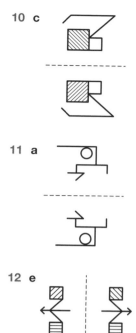

11 a

12 e

Focus test 16 (pages 34–35)

1 **c** The second shape is a square grid with each of the shapes from the first part in each of the squares; the first and third shapes are in the first column and retain their shading; the second and fourth shapes become white with the original shading style surrounding the white shape.

2 **d** The number of circles in the first part equals the number of sides of the polygon in the second shape; the number of white circles with no line through equals the number of plain white circles in the second shape.

3 **c** The second shape is a rhombus with the small white shape that was inside placed below the diamond, and the two black shapes that were inside the first shape moved to the outside left and right vertices. The one cross in the first shape increases to three inside the second shape.

4–8 Sometimes, the code has three letters. Even though the explanations below give the letters in order, you may find it easier to identify features linking the second or third letter and then move back to the other letters.

4 **d** The first letter represents the shape of the 'shield' (D has a curved base, E has a pointed base so, by deduction, F has an angular base); the second letter represents the shading of the circle (A is horizontal lines, B is vertical lines, C is cross-hatch lines); the third letter represents the shading of the square in the top right corner (X has diagonal lines, Y is half white/half black so, by deduction, Z is divided into quarters with opposite quarters shaded with diagonal lines).

5 **b** The first letter represents the angles of the short lines at the top of the shapes (A has the lines pointing inwards, B has the lines diagonally pointing out, C has horizontal lines); the second letter represents the style of shading (L is diagonal line shading, M is dashes); the third letter represents the height of the shading (Y is high, X is medium so, by deduction, Z is short).

6 **e** The first letter represents the number of curved projections at the top of the circle (A is 5, B is 3); the second letter represents the shading of the small circles on a line at the base of the shape (P all white, Q all black, R both black and white); the third letter represents the number of small circles at the bottom of the shape (X is 4, Y is 3 so, by deduction, Z is 2).

7 **e** Along the rows the lines in the squares follow the repeating sequence of 'uphill' diagonal line–crossed lines–'downhill' diagonal line, progressing along the rows and moving down the rows from left to right. Another way of looking at this sequence is triangle–quarter-shaded–triangle where the black shaded quarter swaps between top and bottom of the square and the lined triangle rotates 90° anticlockwise each time it appears in the sequence.

8 **b** Each line pattern in the square at the left end of each row is doubled in the second square, and tripled in the third square along the row.

9 **b** The shape in the outer corner of the outer triangles is the same as the shape in the opposite corner of the inner triangle.

10 e    11 c

12 a

EXPANDED ANSWERS

1 **b** Both of the shapes on the left are triangles with a small circle inside and a zig-zag line that crosses all three sides of the triangle; there is the same number of short lines across one end of the zig-zag as there are sections in the zig-zag.

2 **d** Both of the shapes on the left are made up of one triangle and two circles with one circle overlapping the triangle.

3 **d** Both of the shapes on the left have seven lines or key features.

4 **c** Both of the shapes on the left have one shape shaded black inside with diagonal line shading around it.

5 **e** Both of the shapes on the left have a small shape touching the middle of a straight line, with a plain or zig-zag 'tail' projecting out on the opposite side of the line.

6 **d** Both of the shapes on the left are made up of four lines which are connected only by right angles.

7 **e** The first shape is rotated by 180°; the black square becomes white and the white circle has an × added to it in the second shape.

8 **b** The second shape has the same number of sections as there are circles in the first shape, with sections shaded in the same way as the circles are shaded.

9 **c** The second shape has a reflection added in. The pattern of the lower triangle is moved into the top left triangle and the pattern in the top triangle is moved to the top right triangle. The bottom left triangle of the second shape has an arrow perpendicular to that in the top right, and a black spot is added to the bottom right triangle.

10 **c** The second shape has the same number of edges as there are short lines in the first shape; the black spots become triangles on the outside of the second shape and the white dot moves inside. The new shape must have five sides with two white dots inside and one black pentagon outside.

11 **b** The small square in the first shape becomes the top left and bottom right quarters of a larger square; the right angle formed by the short line in the first shape changes to a 45° angle and the diagonal line in the first shape is lengthened in the second shape.

12 **a** The inner shape in the first pattern becomes the outer shape and larger, with the line style of the first outer shape repeated on the inside of the second shape.

13 **a** Black spots are progressively removed from the pattern, working from the top and down the diagonal rows; the decrease starts from the top edge of each row.

14 **e** A pair of L-shapes with semicircles alternates with a plain pair of L shapes. Within each pair they rotated by 180°. In each semi-circle pair, the direction of the long side of the L changes as well. All of the L-shapes have two small circles at the end of the longer line, the shading of which follows the repeating pattern of white–black/white–black–black/white– etc.

15 **b** The shading of the rectangles follows the repeating pattern of 'uphill' diagonal lines–'downhill' diagonal lines–cross-hatch lines. The zig-zag lines with a black circle at one end alternate with a narrower zig-zag with no circle; the wider zig-zag also alternates in its orientation each time.

16 **b** The visible circumference of the circle decreases by 45° each time reducing the length of the curved line; the reversed L-shape at the base follows the repeating pattern of angled to the left–straight below–angled to the right–straight below.

17 **c** The pattern of parallel horizontal lines progressively 'moves up' the shape with the longest line moving up one position each time. The semi-circle on the vertical line progressively moves up in line with the longest horizontal line, alternating with a triangle that remains in the same position line each time.

18 **e** The number of loops or circles on the curly line decreases by one each time from the right end; the black circle alternates with a white circle and the other circle alternates between a dot and a cross.

19–24 Sometimes, the code has three letters. Even though the explanations below give the letters in order, you may find it easier to identify features linking the second or third letter and then move back to the other letters.

19 **c** The first letter represents the line style (A is straight, B is dashed, C is zig-zag, D is curved); the second letter represents the number of lines in the pattern (X is 3, Y is 2, Z is 1).

20 **b** The first letter represents the part of the oval shape that is shaded (A is the two sections outside the large shape, C is the section inside the large shape so, by deduction, B is the whole of the oval shape); the second letter represents the larger shape (X is an oval, Y is a circle, Z is a square).

21 d The first letter represents the arrow style of the top line (A is an open arrow head, B is a black triangle, C is a white triangle); the second letter represents the pattern at the end of the third line down (L ends with a T-shape, M has a white triangle); the third letter represents the shading of the square on the bottom line (R is white, S is black so, by deduction, T is a cross).

22 b The first letter represents the shapes within the square (A has domed shapes, B has black jagged shapes, C has triangles); the second letter represents the pattern along the top bar (E has white circles, F has black circles); the third letter represents the shading within the square (P is diagonal lines, Q is cross-hatched lines).

23 a The first letter represents the shading of the small shape within the triangle (A is white, B has diagonal lines, C is black); the second letter represents the side of the rectangle with the patterned line (G on the left side, H on the right); the third letter represents the pattern on the side of the rectangle (X is large zig-zags, Y is a small 'cut out', Z is small zig-zag lines).

24 c The first letter represents the position of the 'tree' on the top edge of the rectangle (M is near the left end, N is at the right end so, by deduction, L is at the left end); the second letter represents the shading of the rectangle (A is black, B is diagonal lines, C is white); the third letter represents the number of pairs of diagonal lines projecting from the vertical line ('branches' on the 'tree') (X is 1, Y is 2, Z is 3).

25 d The face with the arrow cannot have the arrow parallel to the base of a U-shape, it will be parallel to the side of a U-shape.

26 c The face with the V-shape is in a line with the L-shape face and the arrow face, so these three cannot all be adjacent in the cube.

27 b When a face with an arrow has the arrow pointing to the open top of a U-shape, then the adjacent 'tree' will be pointing down, not up.

28 e When one of the V-shapes points to the side of the U-shape, the adjacent V-shape will point up not down as in cube **e**.

29 a The two faces with triangles have the two triangles pointing towards each other, in cube **a** one triangle points to the side of the other triangle.

30 d The face with the U-shape will be to the right of the face with the arrow when the face with the black spot is below the arrow.

31 e The small shape follows the repeating pattern of black circle–white circle–cross from row to row; the small straight line moves along the side of the square as it progresses along each row.

32 b The patterns in the corners of the inner square of the grid are the two adjacent outer patterns combined.

33 e The three outer triangles have a black spot at the top and, if the inner triangle rotated by 120°, the small triangle adjacent to the outer triangles gives the shading style of the circle.

34 c The connected line of spots alternates between black and white and increases from one to six around the grid; the dashed lines along the outer line repeats the increasing pattern from one to three.

35 d Along each row of the grid the black bar alternates between the top and the bottom of each square; the line pattern goes from one to two to three lines and back to two then one across the rows.

36 d The shapes decrease by one progressively in each column The missing shape needs two lines in the bottom because they decrease from three to two to one in an upward diagonal direction.

37 a

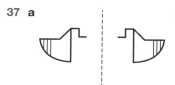

38 e

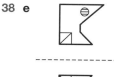

39 b

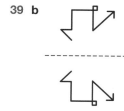

40 a

41 d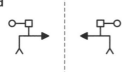

42 e

43 b

44 c

45 e

46 d

47 d

48 e

Mixed paper 2 (pages 44–51)

1 **c** Both of the shapes on the left are quadrilaterals with both a circle and an L-shape with equal length 'arms' within the rectangle and an arrow crossing two sides of it.

2 **d** Both of the shapes on the left have two triangles, one with plain lines and one with dashed lines.

3 **c** Both of the L-shapes on the left have a black spot within them, a three-lined zig-zag line and a short arrow pointing inwards from one corner.

4 **e** Both of the shapes on the left comprise four elements of the same style or shape.

5 **d** Both of the shapes on the left have a triangle and a shape with two straight and two curved edges.

6 **b** Both of the shapes on the left are made up of three identical shapes, one large and two small.

7 **d** The second pattern in each pair is a reflection of the first shape with horizontal line shading changed to vertical line shading.

8 **c** The second pattern is a circle with the number of crosses in the first pattern of the pair being the number of small shapes within the circle, the small shapes match the shape in the top right triangle and have the same shading style as the bottom right triangle of the first pattern.

9 **e** The top left and bottom right outer small shapes in the first pattern move inside a smaller square and swap shading styles to give the second pattern.

10 **d** The Z-shape of the first pattern becomes narrower and taller; the number of arrow heads at one end doubles and the black circles become white to give the second pattern.

11 **c** The U-shapes in the first pattern rotate through 180°; the overlapping shape with dashed lines moves outside the U-shape but adjoining the middle line of the U-shape; the outline becomes solid and line shading is added.

12 **b** The white shape at the lower end of the first pattern gives the shape for the second pattern, the shading of the top shape gives its shading style and the number of loops gives the number of those shapes that form the second pattern.

13 **c** The single vertical line alternates between being a dashed line and a solid line; the number of dashed lines in the triangle increases by one along the sequence and then decreases by one.

14 **a** The horizontal L-shapes alternate with the squares and in their orientation; they also alternate in having black spots or short lines across the longer arm of the L, with the

number of those features decreasing by one along the sequence.

15 **c** The number of joined lines in the pattern decreases by one each time with alternate shapes having short diagonal lines pointing inwards or outwards.

16 **b** The semi-circle and triangle at the base of the rectangle alternate with shading following the repeating pattern of lined–black–white; the pattern at the top of the rectangle increases by adding a line or circle in turn along the sequence.

17 **d** The arrow head alternates between a plain line and a black triangle, and the short line projecting from the circle moves 45° anticlockwise around the circle at each step.

18 **c** The number of lines in the zig-zag pattern increases by one each time and the number of connected circles alternates between two and three along the sequence.

19–24 Sometimes, the code has three letters. Even though the explanations below give the letters in order, you may find it easier to identify features linking the second or third letter and then move back to the other letters.

19 **e** The first letter represents the line style of the circle (D is solid line with dashed inner line, E is double dashed line so, by deduction, F is a double solid line); the second letter represents the inner shape (R is a triangle, S is a square, T is a rhombus); the third letter represents the shading of the inner shape (Y is black, Z is white).

20 **c** The first letter represents the orientation of the two lines below the horizontal arrow (A is an L-shape, B is an inverted T-shape, C is a reverse L-shape); the second letter represents the arrowhead style (E is a white triangle, F is a black triangle so, by deduction, G is an open arrow head); the third letter represents the pattern in the small square (X is a cross, Y is an 'uphill' diagonal line so, by deduction, Z is a 'downhill' diagonal line).

21 **a** The first letter represents the shading of the top left rectangle (A is black, B is diagonal lines so, by deduction, C is cross-hatch lines); the second and third letters represent the shading of the two rectangles on the right side of the shape (LS is vertical stripes above and black below, MT is black above and cross-grid lines below).

22 **e** The first letter represents the position of the black triangle (A is the top left corner of the square, B is the top right corner); the second letter represents the number of C-shapes in the square (P is 3, Q is 4, R is 5); the third letter represents the shape on the bottom left corner (X is a triangle, Y is a circle, by

deduction, Z is a square).

23 **e** The first letter represents the shape (A is a kite, B is a trapezium, C is a regular rhombus); the second letter represents the position of the circle (D inside the shape, E across a line); the third letter represents the number of arrows (X is 1, Z is 3 so, by deduction, Y is 2).

24 **b** The first letter represents the outer shape (A is a circle, C is a quadrilateral so, by deduction, B is a triangle); the second letter represents the inner shape (F is a heart, G is a bow, H is a spade); the third letter represents the shading of the inner shape (R is lined shading, S is black so, by deduction, T is white).

25 **d** The faces with the plain arrow, the spot and the L-shape are all in a line in the net, so they cannot all meet at one corner of the cube.

26 **d** The open side of the C-shape is not adjacent to the top of the heart shape in the net.

27 **c** When there is an arrow face beside the top of the heart face and one beside it, then the arrow beside it will point away from the top of the heart not towards it.

28 **a** When the V-shape face points to the black triangle then the adjacent U-face will be to the right of the inverted V-shape not to its left.

29 **b** The arrow face points away from the face with the heart towards the crescent, not towards the top of the heart.

30 **e** The single arrow points away from the face with the double arrow, not towards it.

31 **d** The shapes in the inner square are a reflection of the shapes in the outer, non-adjacent rectangle at the end of the same row.

32 **b** The sequence is 5–4–3 across each row so the boxes along the bottom row of the grid have that number of lines in the zig-zag with a black dot.

33 **d** One side of the square pattern is removed in successive grid squares both along the long rows or down the long columns of the grid.

34 **b** The outer three triangles of the grid are identical.

35 **e** The row of spots on the outside edge increases by one moving clockwise from the top of the hexagon; the line coming out from the centre alternates between having a back spot or an L-shape with its short side projecting round clockwise.

36 **d** The shapes in each diagonal across the grid (from top left to bottom right) are the same, with the shading alternating; the shapes follow a repeating pattern in the opposite direction (top right to bottom left) which is X-shape–half-shaded circle–X-shape–square–triangle.

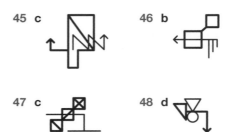

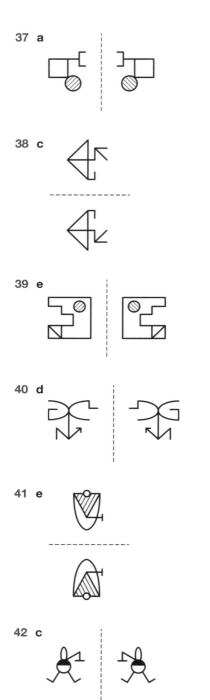

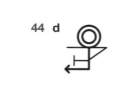

37 **a**

38 **c**

39 **e**

40 **d**

41 **e**

42 **c**

43 **a**

44 **d**

45 **c**

46 **b**

47 **c**

48 **d**

Mixed paper 3 (pages 52–59)

1 **b** Both of the shapes on the left have a curved arrow with no line at the end and a white circle is the first shape after the arrowhead.

2 **e** Both of the larger circles on the left contain a circle inside a square and they both have an S-shape inside.

3 **d** Both of the shapes on the left have a single-headed arrow in the square and a circle at the opposite end of the adjacent rectangle.

4 **c** Both of the shapes on the left are polygons with a black triangle within them, a white triangle on the outside and a triangle across the line with the section inside the polygon shaded grey.

5 **e** Both of the shapes on the left are squares with a straight dashed line and a double curved line crossing the square.

6 **a** Both of the shapes on the left are made up of three straight lines and three circles.

7 **a** The second shape of the pair is the same as the first shape though larger and shaded black, with the lines of each side extended and no crosses underneath.

8 **d** The second shape is a polygon with the same number of sides as there are lines in the first zig-zag, and with one black spot less than there are sides of the polygon.

9 **e** The second shape has one less U-shape in the line, with a row of inverted U-shapes above it, 'capping' the junctions where the U-shapes on the lower line join.

10 **b** The second shape is a quartered square with dividing lines following the orientation of the grid lines in the first shape; it contains black spots in the same number of quarters as there are black squares outside the first shape.

11 **c** The second pattern is the same shape as the left hand small shape in the first pattern, with edges in the style of the single line and containing the right hand small shape from the first pattern.

12 **c** The number of shapes in the first pattern gives the number of white sections to the second shape with the number of black parts in the first shape being the same in the second

pattern. Each part of the new shape touches at least one other. Each of the new white sections contains a small cross.

13 **e** The small square follows a repeating pattern of moving up the larger square in three steps with shading swapping between black and diagonal; in alternate squares there is a line making a triangle in the bottom right corner; and the central short 'pin' rotates 45° clockwise each time along the sequence.

14 **e** The pattern grows along the sequence with the addition of a small triangle below each circle, a circle onto each triangle point and then another row of triangles.

15 **c** The line pattern alternates with the irregular shape; in a pair of a line patterns and an irregular shape, there are two spots and one curly line alternating with one spot and two curly lines.

16 **b** The shape grows with the addition of one line each time, firstly extending the zigzag pattern down then back up on the right side of the shape, line by line.

17 **b** The small circles alternate with the larger circles; the line shading of the larger circles follows the repeating sequence of parallel lines rotating through 45° anticlockwise at each step.

18 **d** The central small horizontal line in the pattern alternates between having a T-shape and a black spot; an additional column of short lines, increasing by one each time, is added to the right of the shape. The orientation of the shape does not change.

19–24 Sometimes, the code has three letters. Even though the explanations below give the letters in order, you may find it easier to identify features linking the second or third letter and then move back to the other letters.

19 **a** The first letter represents the arrowhead (A is a line, B is a white triangle so, by deduction, C is a black triangle); the second letter represents the shading of the section of the small circle that is inside the larger shape (P is white, Q is grey); the third letter represents the style of shading for the circle (L is grey, M is white, N is black).

20 **e** The first letter represents the number and position of the dashed lines in the large quadrilateral (A has two opposite lines dashed, B has two adjacent lines dashed so, by deduction, C has three sides dashed); the second letter represents the number of small shapes in the pattern (G is 3, H is 4); the third letter represents one of the small shapes having shading (S is yes, T is no).

21 **c** The first letter represents the line style in the larger kite shape (E has dashed and plain lines,

D has bold lines); the second letter represents the number of lines crossing the larger shape (L is 1, M is 2 so, by deduction, N is 3); the third letter represents the second shape in the pattern (X is a circle, Y is a triangle, Z is a quadrilateral).

22 **d** The first letter represents the position of the black circle (A outside the shape, B inside the shape, C on the outline of the shape); the second letter represents the number of lines making the shape (E is 6, G is 8 so, by deduction, F is 7); the third letter represents the line at the base of the pattern (X is a line, Y is an L-shape).

23 **b** The first letter represents the shading of the small circle (A is black, B is white, C has a cross); the second letter represents the orientation of the small line projecting from the circle (J points up, K points to the right, L points down so, by deduction, M points to the left); the third letter represents the line style at the end of the curved line (R is a plain I-shape, S has a V-shape, T has a T-shape).

24 **d** The first letter represents the shape at the end of the zig-zag line (A is a black circle, B is a white circle, C is a white triangle so, by deduction, D is a black triangle); the second letter represents the number of short lines crossing the zig-zag (K is 8, L is 7, M is 6).

25 **d** The open end of the V-shape will be along the edge shared with the face with the black circle, not the face with the X-shape.

26 **b** Both faces with an arrow will have the arrow pointing away from the face with the heart not towards it.

27 **c** When two faces with arrows are adjacent the arrows will either be perpendicular to each other or parallel pointing in the same direction, not one arrow pointing each way.

28 **c** The open end of the V-shape will be along the edge shared with the face with the point of the heart, not the face with the U-shape.

29 **b** On the face with the partly shaded X, the black triangle is adjacent to the face with the white circle, not the face with the arrow.

30 **a** The face with parallel lines would be adjacent to the edge along the side of the smiley face, rather than next to the top of the smiley face.

31 **c** The cross–white circle–black circle follow a repeating pattern along each row; the line patterns build in the same way across each row; also, the line pattern in the squares along the top row of the grid are reflected along the squares in the bottom row if there was a mirror line through the middle row.

32 **c** The circles in each pair of squares on the outside of the grid have the same shading as the adjacent inner triangle.

33 **e** The sequences follow diagonally from top left to bottom right. The small squares move anticlockwise round the grid squares and the pattern in the small squares on the left of the grid follows the reverse order of the pattern in the squares on the right of the grid.

34 **c** The shape in the outer triangles of the grid is the same as that in the opposite corner of the inner triangle but increased in size.

35 **a** There are two small black triangles in the outer corners of alternate triangles in the central hexagon; this means only option **e** can be the correct answer.

36 **e** The number of shapes or crosses down the left side of each rectangle in the grid increases by one down each column; each column has the same shading style for the inner shapes.

37 **d**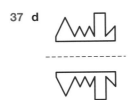

38 **e**

39 **d**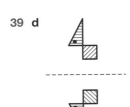

40 **b**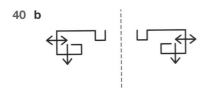

41 **c**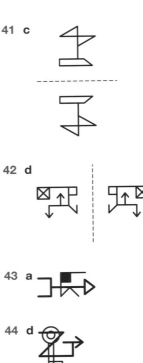

42 **d**

43 **a**

44 **d**

45 **b**

46 **e**

47 **e**

48 **d**

A16

6

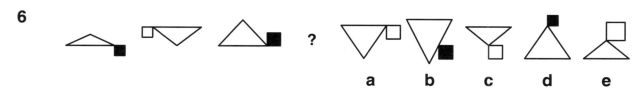

	a	b	c	d	e

Which code matches the last pattern on the right? Circle the letter.

7

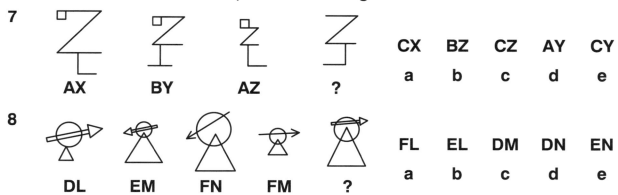

AX   BY   AZ   ?

CX	BZ	CZ	AY	CY
a	b	c	d	e

8

DL   EM   FN   FM   ?

FL	EL	DM	DN	EN
a	b	c	d	e

Which cube cannot be made from the net on the left? Circle the letter.

9

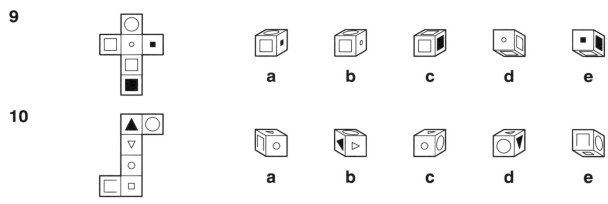

a   b   c   d   e

10

a   b   c   d   e

Which one completes the grid? Circle the letter.

11

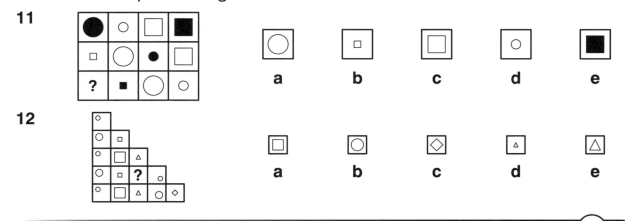

a   b   c   d   e

12

a   b   c   d   e

Focus test 15

In this test the questions have at least two factors that vary, for example, shape and position. They also include extra elements that are not significant to the question. These elements are there to distract you so, once you have identified them, they can be ignored.

Which one belongs to the group on the left? Circle the letter.

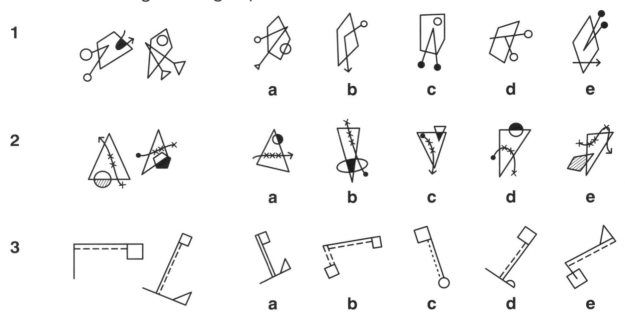

1   a   b   c   d   e

2   a   b   c   d   e

3   a   b   c   d   e

Which one comes next? Circle the letter.

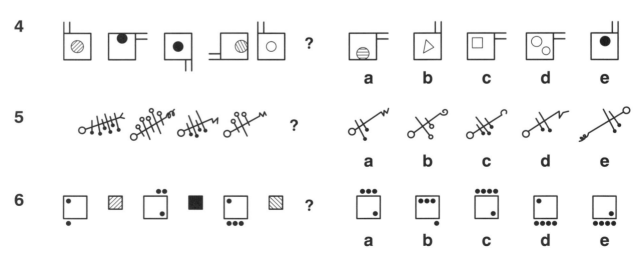

4   a   b   c   d   e

5   a   b   c   d   e

6   a   b   c   d   e

Which cube cannot be made from the net on the left? Circle the letter.

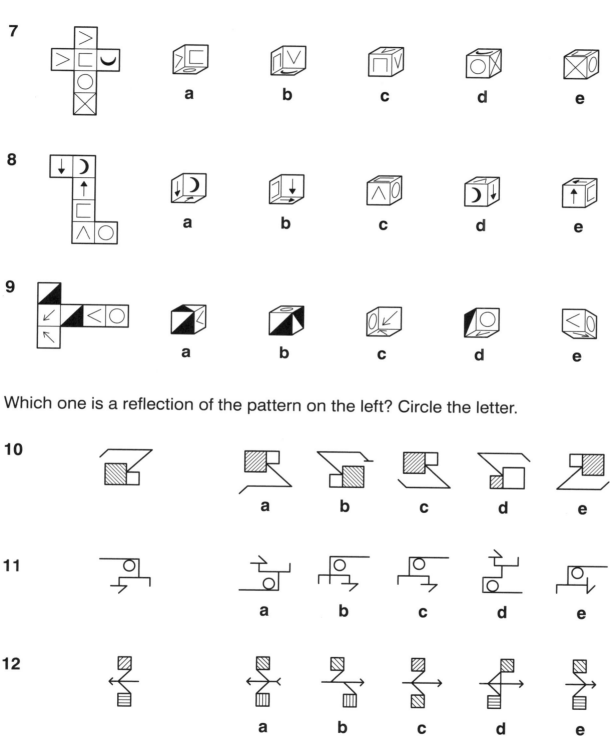

7

a   b   c   d   e

8

a   b   c   d   e

9

a   b   c   d   e

Which one is a reflection of the pattern on the left? Circle the letter.

10

a   b   c   d   e

11

a   b   c   d   e

12

a   b   c   d   e

Look carefully at the patterns given to identify which elements are important and necessary to help you find the right answer. There will usually be two or more of these. There may also be features that are not significant. Check these carefully and then ignore them.

Which one completes the second pair in the same way as the first pair? Circle the letter.

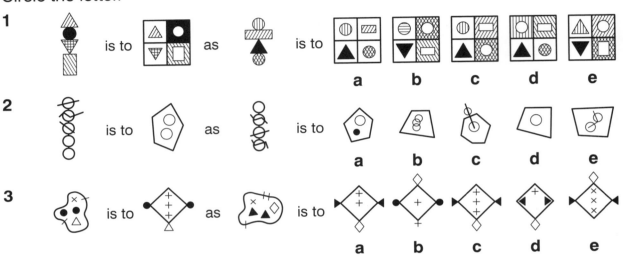

Which code matches the last pattern on the right? Circle the letter.

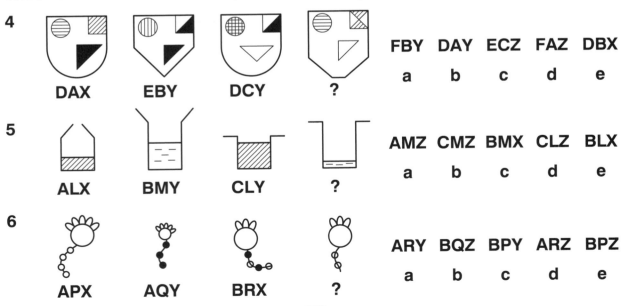

Which one completes the grid? Circle the letter.

7

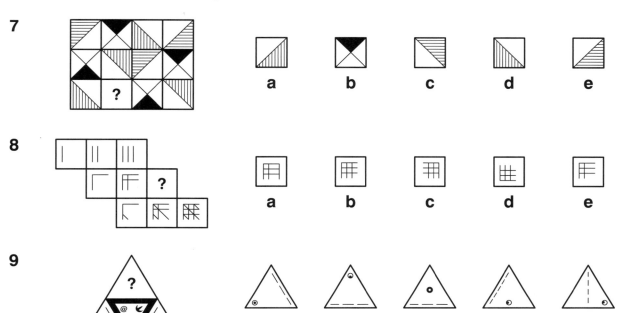

8

9

Which pattern is made by combining the two shapes on the left? Circle the letter.

10 ... and ...

11 ... and ...

12 ... and ...

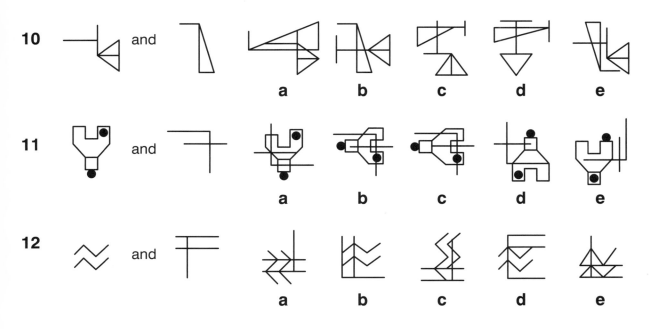

Mixed paper 1

Which one belongs to the group on the left? Circle the letter.

Example

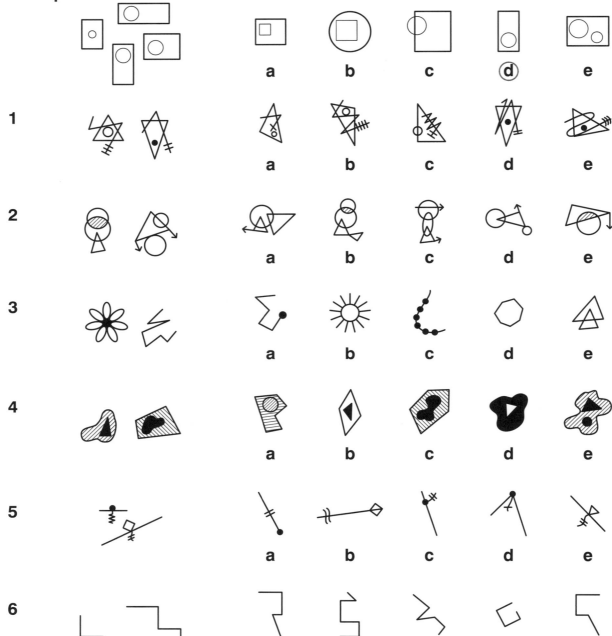

Which one completes the second pair in the same way as the first pair? Circle the letter.

Example

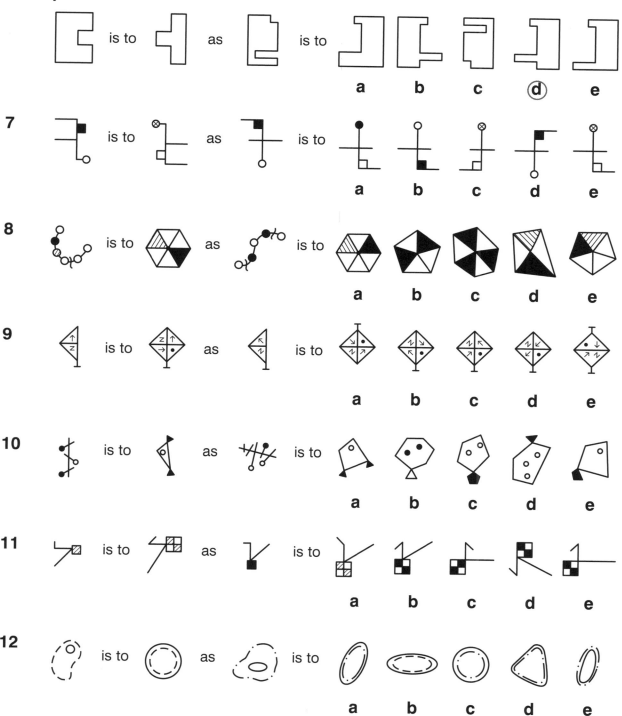

Which one comes next? Circle the letter.

Example

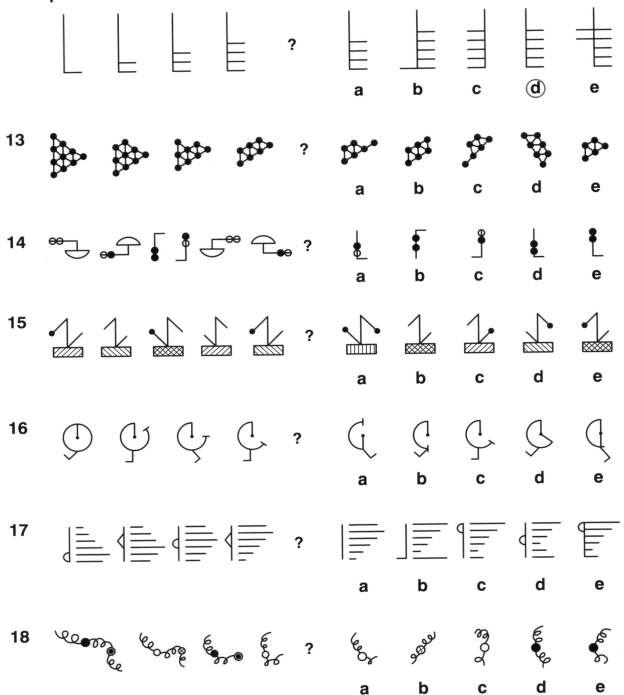

Which code matches the last pattern on the right? Circle the letter.

Example

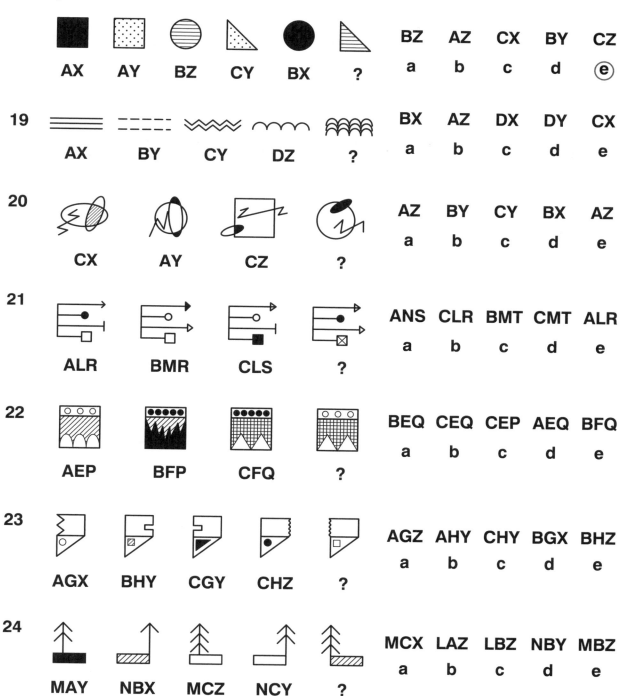

	AX	AY	BZ	CY	BX	?

BZ AZ CX BY CZ
a   b   c   d   (e)

19 AX BY CY DZ ?

BX AZ DX DY CX
a   b   c   d   e

20 CX AY CZ ?

AZ BY CY BX AZ
a   b   c   d   e

21 ALR BMR CLS ?

ANS CLR BMT CMT ALR
a   b   c   d   e

22 AEP BFP CFQ ?

BEQ CEQ CEP AEQ BFQ
a   b   c   d   e

23 AGX BHY CGY CHZ ?

AGZ AHY CHY BGX BHZ
a   b   c   d   e

24 MAY NBX MCZ NCY ?

MCX LAZ LBZ NBY MBZ
a   b   c   d   e

Which cube cannot be made from the net on the left? Circle the letter.

Example

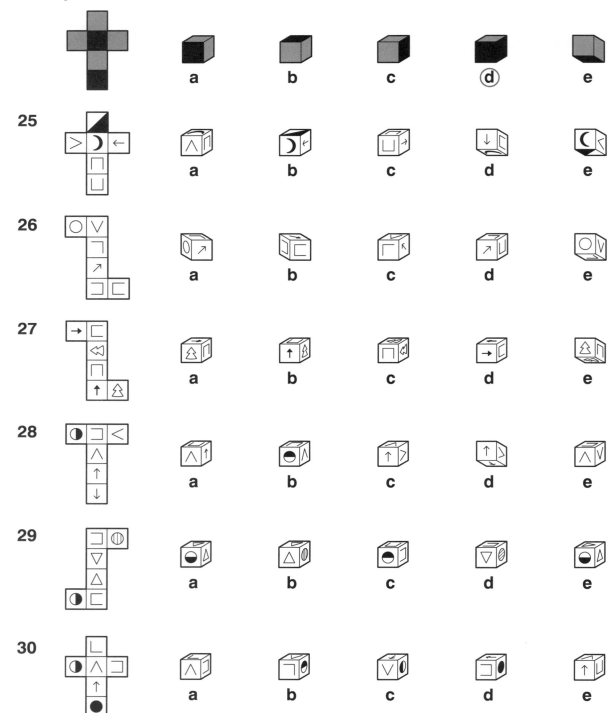

a   b   c   d   e

25

a   b   c   d   e

26

a   b   c   d   e

27

a   b   c   d   e

28

a   b   c   d   e

29

a   b   c   d   e

30

a   b   c   d   e

Which one completes the grid? Circle the letter.

Example

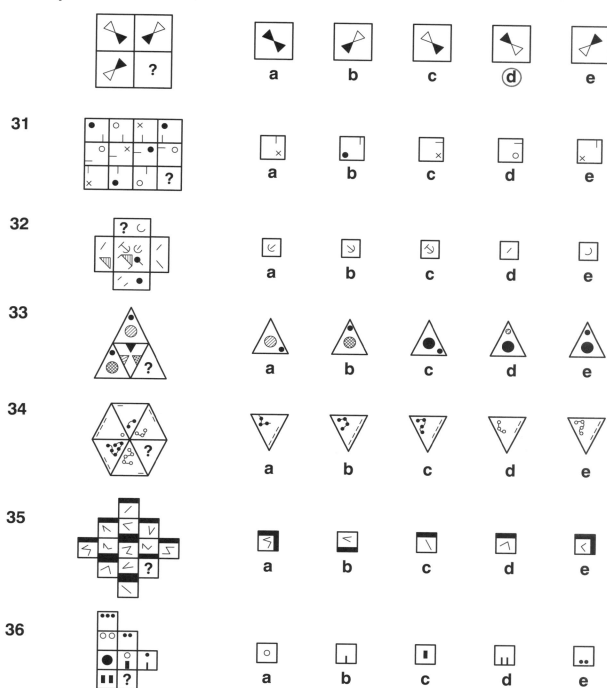

31

32

33

34

35

36

Which one is a reflection of the pattern on the left? Circle the letter.

Example

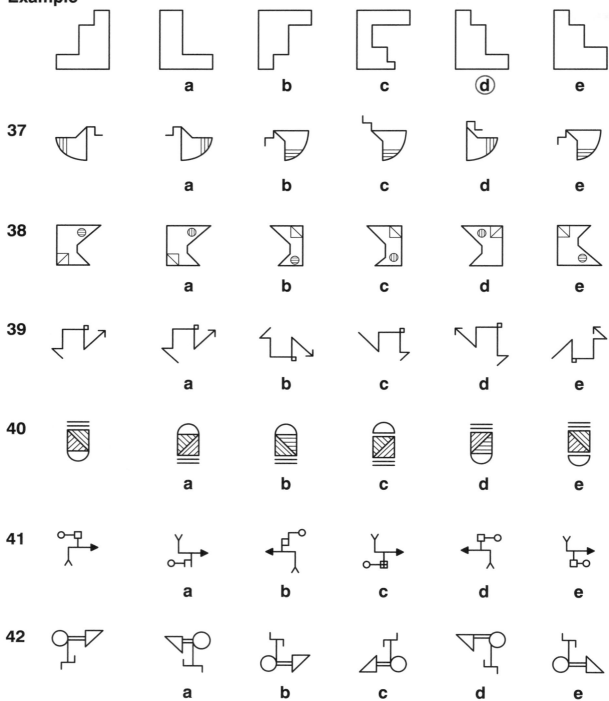

37

38

39

40

41

42

Which pattern is made by combining the two shapes on the left?
Circle the letter.

Example

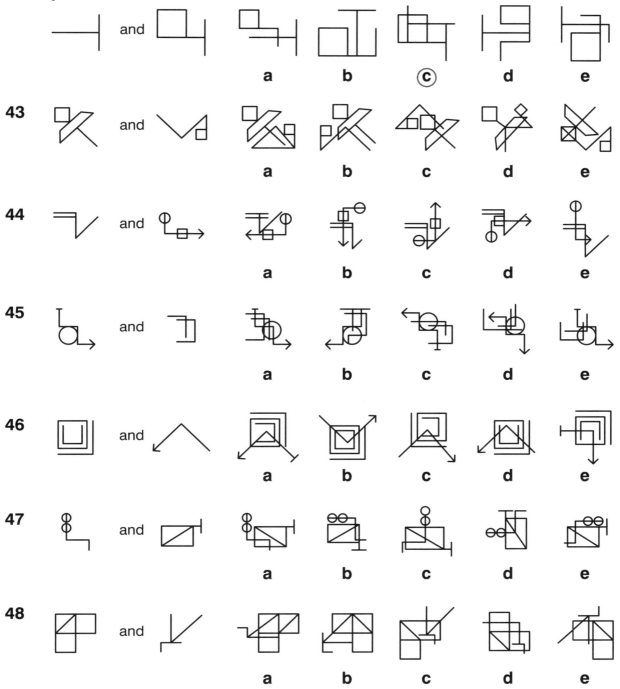

a   b   ⓒ   d   e

43

a   b   c   d   e

44

a   b   c   d   e

45

a   b   c   d   e

46

a   b   c   d   e

47

a   b   c   d   e

48

a   b   c   d   e

Mixed paper 2

Which one belongs to the group on the left? Circle the letter.

Example

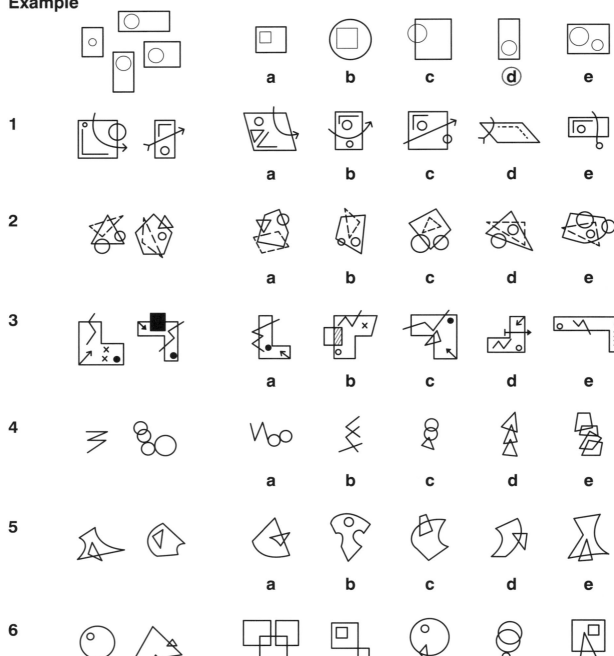

Which one completes the second pair in the same way as the first pair? Circle the letter.

Example

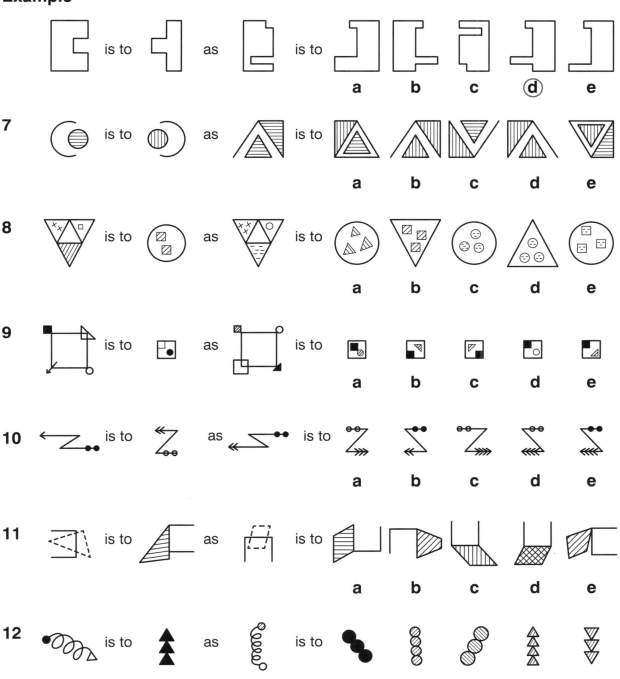

Which one comes next? Circle the letter.

Example

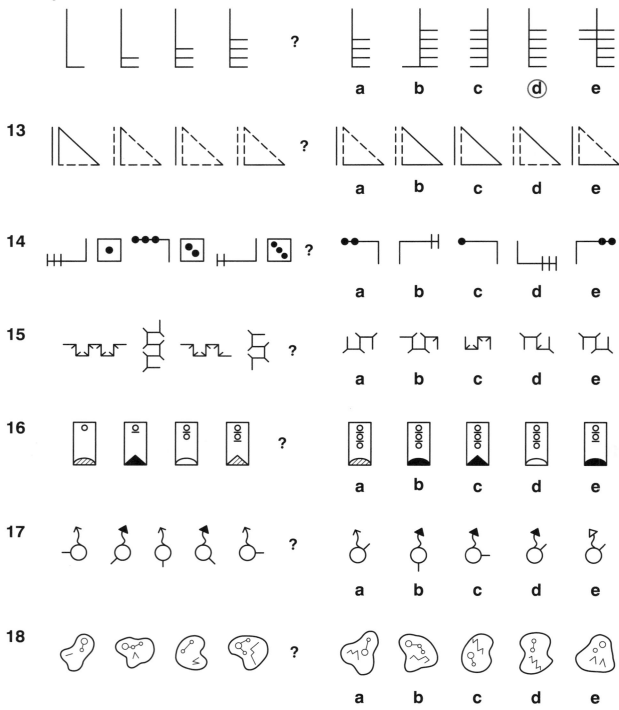

13

14

15

16

17

18

Which code matches the last pattern on the right? Circle the letter.

Example

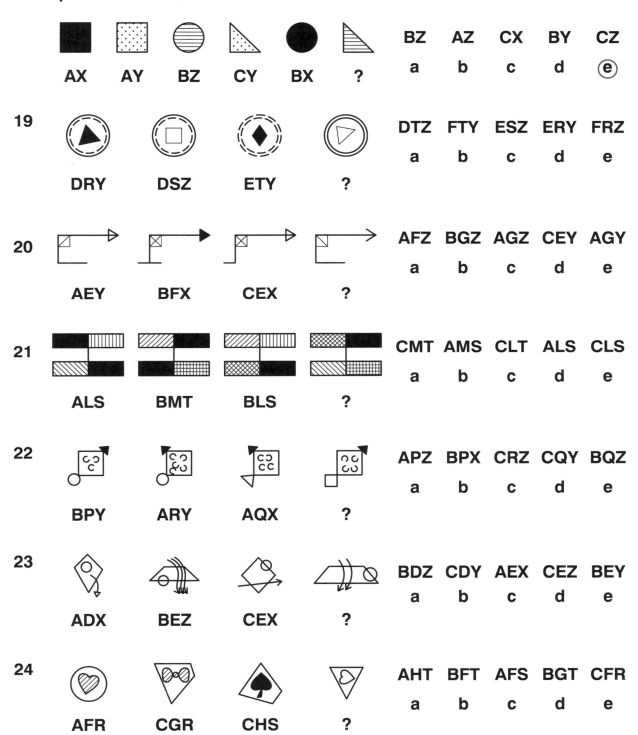

BZ	AZ	CX	BY	CZ
a	b	c	d	(e)

AX   AY   BZ   CY   BX   ?

19

DTZ	FTY	ESZ	ERY	FRZ
a	b	c	d	e

DRY   DSZ   ETY   ?

20

AFZ	BGZ	AGZ	CEY	AGY
a	b	c	d	e

AEY   BFX   CEX   ?

21

CMT	AMS	CLT	ALS	CLS
a	b	c	d	e

ALS   BMT   BLS   ?

22

APZ	BPX	CRZ	CQY	BQZ
a	b	c	d	e

BPY   ARY   AQX   ?

23

BDZ	CDY	AEX	CEZ	BEY
a	b	c	d	e

ADX   BEZ   CEX   ?

24

AHT	BFT	AFS	BGT	CFR
a	b	c	d	e

AFR   CGR   CHS   ?

(47)

Which cube cannot be made from the net on the left? Circle the letter.

Example

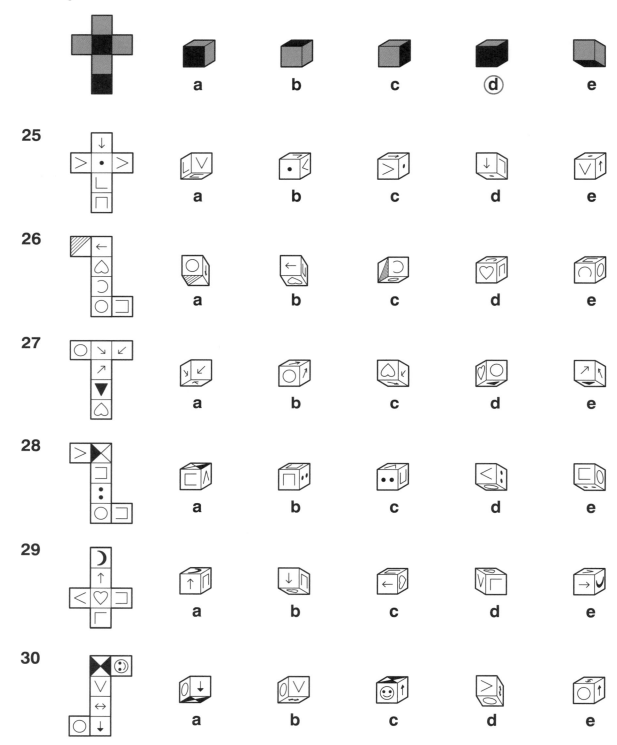

25

a   b   c   d   e

26

a   b   c   d   e

27

a   b   c   d   e

28

a   b   c   d   e

29

a   b   c   d   e

30

a   b   c   d   e

Which one completes the grid? Circle the letter.

Example

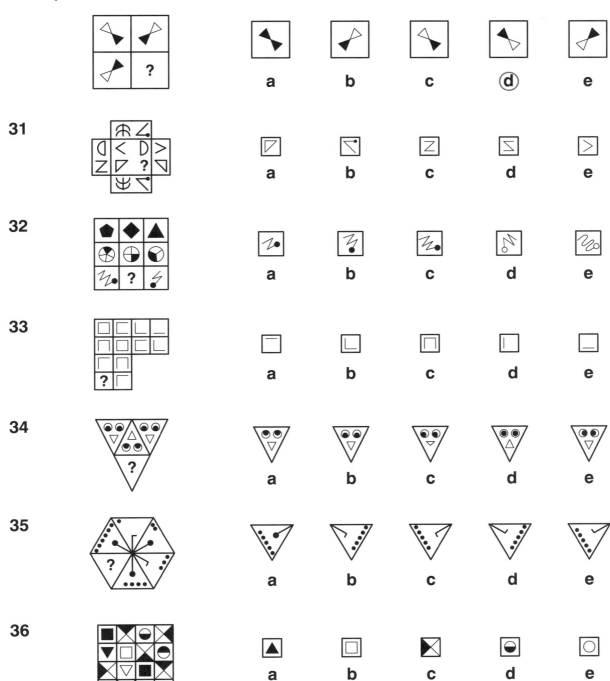

31

a b c d e

32

a b c d e

33

a b c d e

34

a b c d e

35

a b c d e

36

a b c d e

Which one is a reflection of the pattern on the left? Circle the letter.

Example

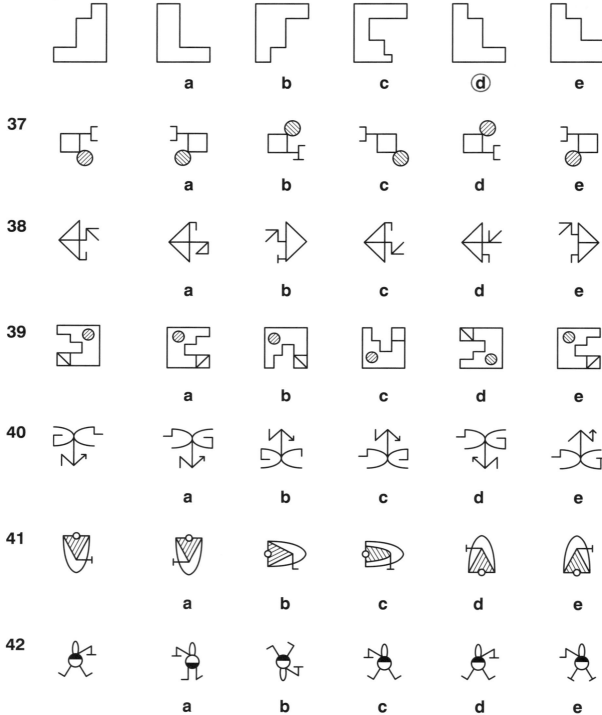

a   **b**   **c**   **d**   **e**

37   **a**   **b**   **c**   **d**   **e**

38   **a**   **b**   **c**   **d**   **e**

39   **a**   **b**   **c**   **d**   **e**

40   **a**   **b**   **c**   **d**   **e**

41   **a**   **b**   **c**   **d**   **e**

42   **a**   **b**   **c**   **d**   **e**

Which pattern is made by combining the two shapes on the left?
Circle the letter.

Example

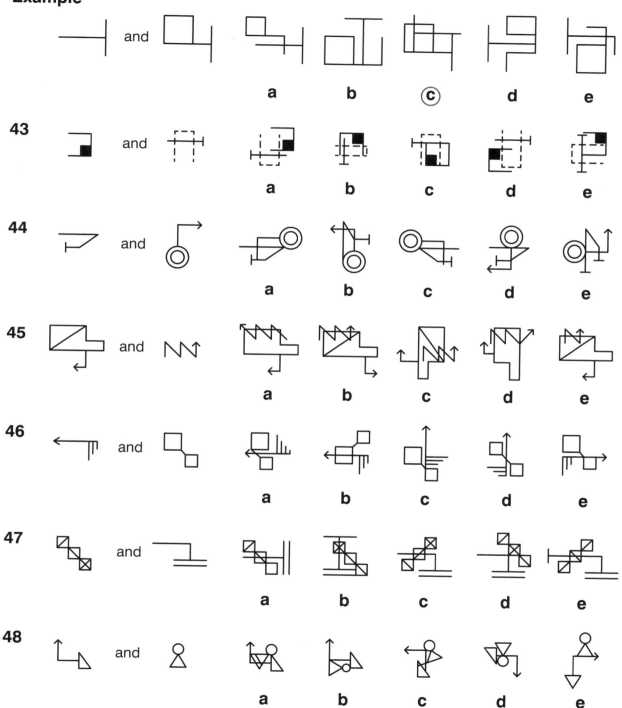

a   b   ⓒ   d   e

43

a   b   c   d   e

44

a   b   c   d   e

45

a   b   c   d   e

46

a   b   c   d   e

47

a   b   c   d   e

48

a   b   c   d   e

Mixed paper 3

Which one belongs to the group on the left? Circle the letter.

Example

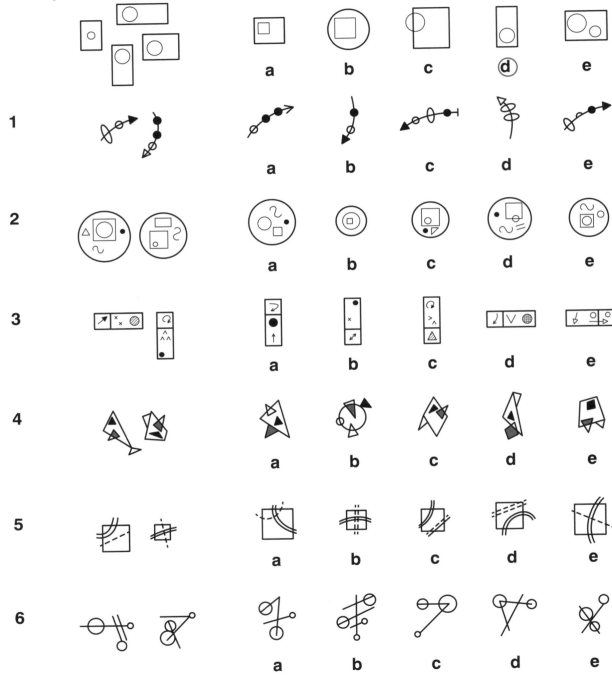

Which one completes the second pair in the same way as the first pair?
Circle the letter.

Example

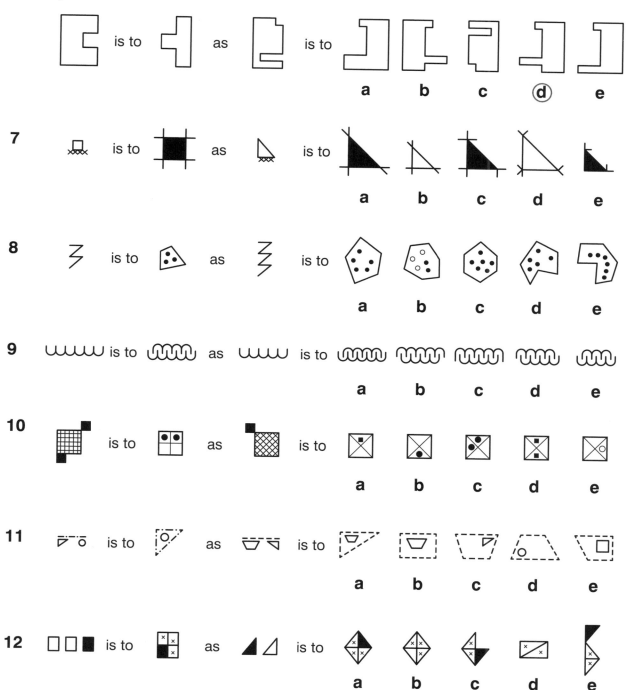

Which one comes next? Circle the letter.

Example

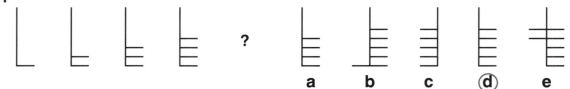

a   b   c   (d)   e

13

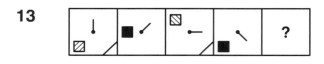 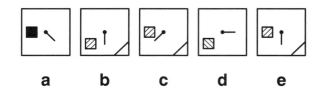

a   b   c   d   e

14

 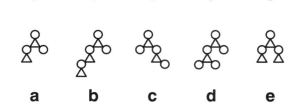

a   b   c   d   e

15

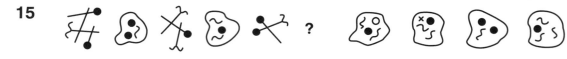 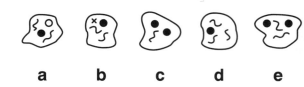

a   b   c   d   e

16

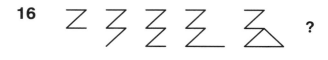 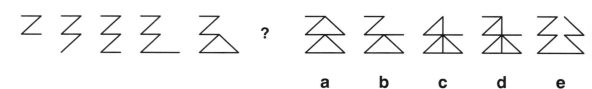

a   b   c   d   e

17

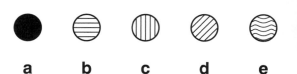

a   b   c   d   e

18

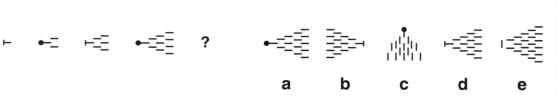

a   b   c   d   e

Which code matches the last pattern on the right? Circle the letter.

Example

AX AY BZ CY BX ?

BZ	AZ	CX	BY	CZ
a	b	c	d	(e)

19

APM BPN AQL ?

CPL	CPN	BPL	BQM	AQM
a	b	c	d	e

20

AHS AGT BGS ?

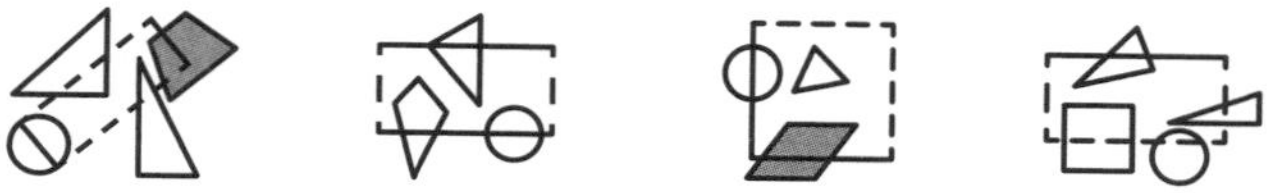

CGT	BHS	AGT	AHT	CHT
a	b	c	d	e

21

DMX ELY EMZ ?

FMY	DNY	DNX	FLZ	ENX
a	b	c	d	e

22

AEX BGY CGX ?

CFX	BGX	AFY	BFY	CEX
a	b	c	d	e

23

AJR BKS BLT CLS ?

CKS	CMR	BJT	ALS	AMT
a	b	c	d	e

24

AK BM CL BL ?

DK	CM	DL	DM	CK
a	b	c	d	e

55

Which cube cannot be made from the net on the left? Circle the letter.

Example

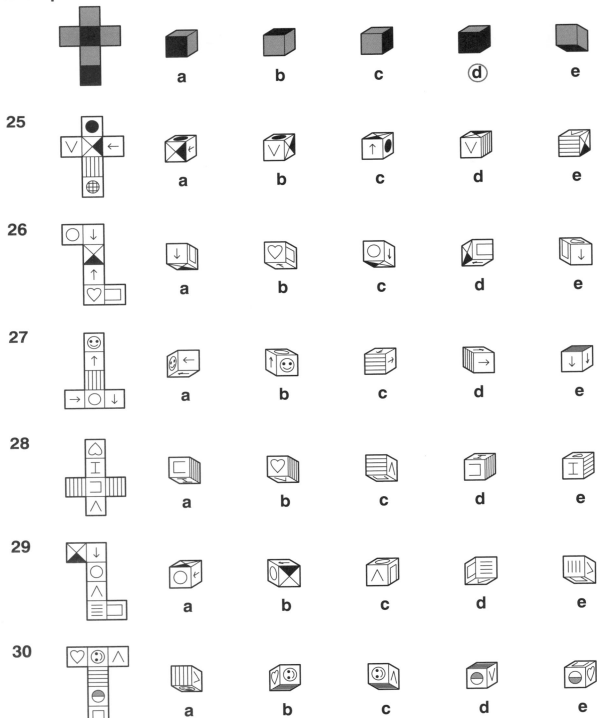

25

26

27

28

29

30

Which one completes the grid? Circle the letter.

Example

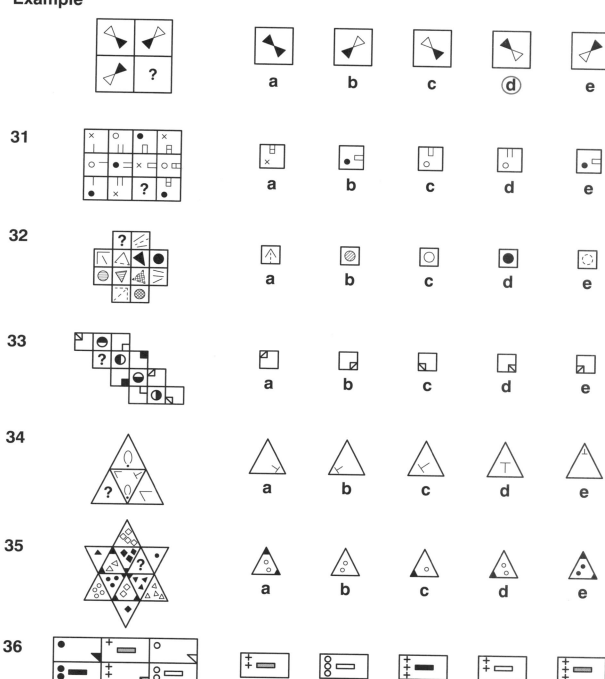

31

32

33

34

35

36

Which one is a reflection of the pattern on the left? Circle the letter.

Example

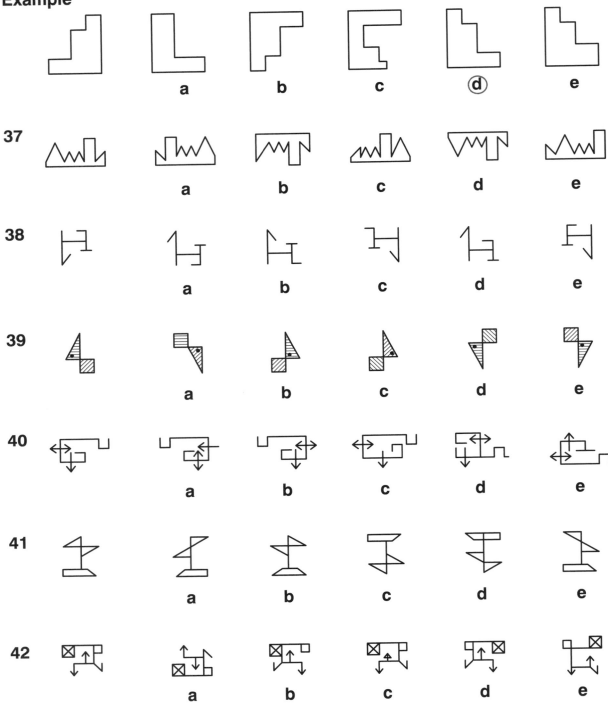

37

38

39

40

41

42

Which pattern is made by combining the two shapes on the left?
Circle the letter.

Example

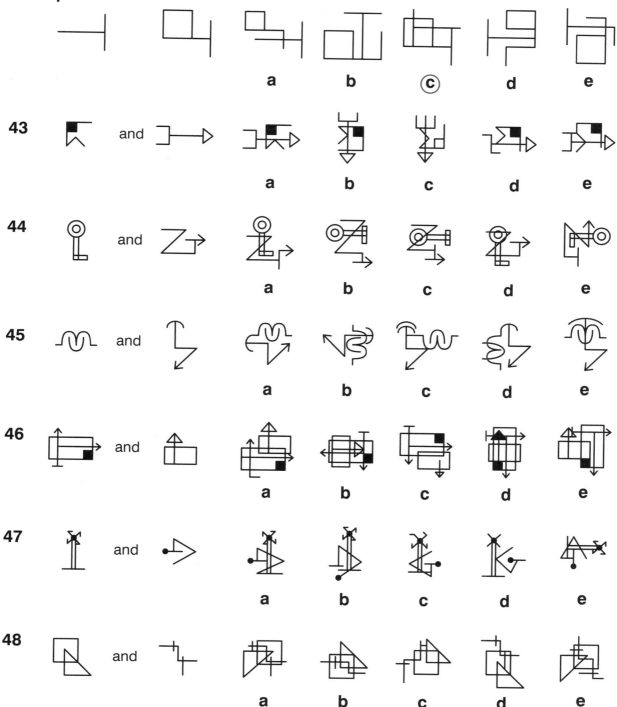

a   b   ⓒ   d   e

43   and

a   b   c   d   e

44   and

a   b   c   d   e

45   and

a   b   c   d   e

46   and

a   b   c   d   e

47   and

a   b   c   d   e

48   and

a   b   c   d   e